Dinosaurs

Dinosaurs

Discoveries • Species • Extinction

Contents

THE MESOZOIC ERA 38

THE CENOZOIC ERA 86

CHAPTER 1

The History of the Earth

Millions of years ago, long before there were people, the Earth was dominated by dinosaurs, many kinds of them. Most of them lived during the Mesozoic era, and died out at the end of the Cretaceous period that brought this era to an end some 65 million years ago.

The dinosaurs were reptiles, which belong to the group of four-legged vertebrates. They and their relatives lived on land, in the water (Ichthyosaurus, Mixosaurus) or in the air (pterosaurs). There were numerous different species, which lived at different periods. Some of them were beasts of prey (Tyranno-saurus, Ichthyosaurus, Deinonychus) while others were herbivores (Brachiosaurus, Apatosaurus). Some were as small as lizards, while others were bigger than elephants. Some walked on two legs (Edmontosaurus), others on all fours (Mamenchisaurus). The marine saurians had adapted their legs into paddles, and the pterosaurs had grown wings with flying membranes. Many dinosaurs wandered around in herds.

The word "dinosaur" is only about 200 years old, but it has become an everyday term and always arouses lively associations. Even today we think of dinosaurs as fearful creatures, looking like dragons and no less dangerous. Placing them in the "timetable" of the Earth's history, we shall try to give some idea of the conditions in which the dinosaurs lived, until, some 65 million years ago, they mysteriously died out.

The Discoveries

Long before the dinosaurs were recognized as a group in their own right there had been numerous finds which could not at first be properly classified. There are written records from China dating back as long ago as the 3rd century AD that so-called "dragon's bones", thought to have magical powers, had been found. But it was not until much later that modern science identified them as remains of dinosaurs.

In 1677 Robert Plot, a professor at Oxford University, wrote an essay in which he described a huge bone which had been found in Oxford-shire. It was the thigh-bone of a huge beast the size of an elephant. At first he thought that the Romans had brought an elephant to Britain during the period of their occupa-tion, but there were no written records of this. After he had examined a real elephant skeleton, he realized that these bones were very different from those found in Oxfordshire. Plot's conclusion was that there must once have been human giants.

In spite of a lot more finds, until about 150 years ago there were no serious scientific insights into dinosaurs. Doubtless the Christian teachings, based on the Bible, had a lot to do with this. After all, they said that God had created the world in seven days, and that all life had started in the Garden of Eden. So why should extinct creatures ever have existed?

The decisive find, which made the existence of giant reptiles official, was made in 1822 by the wife of the doctor and fossil-collector Gideon Algernon Mantell. In Sussex she found numerous fossil teeth. Her husband said they belonged to an animal that must have been very similar to the iguana, a lizard from America. As a result, he called the new animal Iguanodon (iguana-tooth). According to his description, it was a clumsy animal with a horn on its nose. As it turned out later, the horn was in fact the Iguanodon's toe.

At the same time, an Englishman called William Buckland was describing fossils found in a quarry not far from Oxford. They looked quite different. These were the backbone and jawbones of a giant lizard, which he called Megalo-saurus (giant lizard). A few years later, Mantell found another huge reptile, which he called Hylaeosaurus. The finds

Excavation of the first mastodon skeleton from a marsh near Newburgh, USA

triggered a treasure hunt throughout the country. But it was not until 1841 that someone came up with the idea that at some time during the Earth's history there had been a period of life that until then had been completely unknown. At a meeting in Plymouth in 1841, the palaeontologist Richard Owen first spoke of the existence of a group of huge extinct animals, far larger than anything known today. He called these creatures "dinosaurs", which means "terrible lizards". He described these huge reptiles at first as giant clumsy monsters walking on all fours.

In 1858, a whole lot of fossil bones were found in a field in the state of New Jersey in the USA. Joseph Leidy, a professor of anatomy from the University of Philadelphia, examined these bones and in his article on them, gave the animal the name Hadrosaurus ("heavy lizard"). It was very similar to the Iguanodon, and in his opinion it walked on two feet, like a bird. This debate about whether these creatures walked on two or four feet went on for some time; more and more fossils were found, some pointing one way, some the other.

A particularly noteworthy find was made in Belgium in 1878. A mass grave of Iguanodons was found in a coal mine – almost 30 complete skeletons. After years of work, it was found that there must have been a gorge here millions of years ago, into which the creatures had fallen to their deaths.

Excavation of gigantic pre-Ice-Age animal bones in the Rocky Mountains, USA, 1878

excavations were going on in Belgium, two Americans were seeking to go one better on the other side of the Atlantic. Edward Drinker Cope and Othniel Marsh were two brilliant scientists, who described and named more than 130 species of dinosaur. They discovered numerous sites in Colorado, Wyoming and Montana where dinosaur bones were buried. Their important discoveries included Brontosaurus (Apatosaurus), Camarasaurus, Diplodocus, Stegosaurus and Allosaurus.

Alongside finds in Belgium, there were many more excavations in Europe in the 19th century. In a quarry in Trossingen in Germany, thousands of bones belonging to Plateosaurus were found. They were about 200 million years old. The impressions of Archaeopteryx, a bird-dinosaur, were also found. In England, France and the Balkans, the excavations revealed skeletons of armoured dinosaurs, and in Provence, they even turned up nests of dinosaur eggs belonging to the species Hypselosaurus. While the

Othniel Charles Marsh (1831–1899)

When land surveys started in Canada, expeditions set off in particular for Red River in Alberta, where Cope had already identified Albertosaurus (hence the name). Here the remains were found of Triceratops, of duck-billed saurians,

Edward Drinker Cope (1840–1897)

and other creatures of the Cretaceous period. In Tanganyika in Africa, the remains of huge dinosaurs were found in 1907. The skeletons included previously unknown species such as the spiny dinosaur Kentrosaurus, and a Brachiosaurus more than 23 metres long and 12 metres tall.

More recent discoveries

In 1993 an amateur fossil collector named Ruben Carolini found the remains of a giant carnivorous dinosaur in Patagonia in southern Argentina: it was named Giganotosaurus carolinii. With a body-length of 13.5 to 14 metres, a skull-length of 1.65 metres and weighing in at about eight tons, it was probably the largest beast of prey ever to roam the Earth, bigger than Tyrannosaurus rex. It's thought to have lived more than 95 million years ago.

Feather-like structures were found on dinosaurs discovered near the Chinese capital Beijing. The dinosaurs themselves, called Sinosauropteryx, were about 60 centimetres in length, and had long tails like lizards. They were dated to the early Cretaceous period, some 130 to 110 million years ago. The feather structures were noted on their necks, backs and tails. They're not thought to have been suitable for flying, so experts think they were to maintain body temperature.

The Continental Drift

Since our Earth was formed some 4.5 billion years ago, it has undergone all sorts of changes. During this unimaginably long period, the map of the Earth has been changing, slowly but steadily. Constant changes in climate, bringing with them wind, rain, ice and sun, have worn down the mountains (erosion) or in other places filled up the valleys (sedimentation).

Deserts and seas formed. Glaciers built up and shaped the rocks beneath them by grinding away at the surface. Rivers were formed that looked for routes to follow through the landscape. But the really big changes have been brought about in the course of millions of years by the movements of the Earth's crust. These are caused by convection currents deep down inside the Earth.

Geologists have discovered that the lithosphere, the upper layer of the Earth's mantle, on which the crust lies, is not in one piece, but consists of a number of rigid plates. These float on the asthenosphere below – that's the fluid part of the Earth's mantle. It is between 70 and 100 kilometres thick. There are six large plates (the American, the Antarctic, the African, the Eurasian, the Pacific and the Indo-Australian). Some of them are more than 65 million square kilometres in area. And they're constantly on the move.

After taking rock samples from the sea-bed and closely examining the various sedimentary layers, geologists have since succeeded in forming a picture of the possible movements and origins of our continents over the past 400 million years. According to this theory, during the Devonian period, which started 408 million years ago and ended 360 million years ago, there was still no North Atlantic, so that North America and Europe formed one continent, which was named Laurasia.

Supercontinent Pangaea

A large southern continent, named Gondwanaland, comprised modern South America, Australia, Africa, India and Antarctica. Certain fossils of early amphibians and reptiles were found only in what was once Laurasia.

Towards the end of the Permian era (290 to 245 million years ago), the two continents joined up to form one supercontinent called Pangaea (Greek for "the whole Earth"). Pangaea lay on both sides of the equator. Temperatures in those days were mild. There were none of the climatic influences that result from inland seas or polar ice-caps.

This was where the dinosaurs began to evolve. They could spread out over the whole continent. Towards the end of the Triassic, Pangaea began to break apart. Seas appeared between the newly forming continents. Even so, there must still have been land bridges at times, because some fossils, e.g. of Brachiosaurus and Stegosaurus, have been found both in North America and Africa.

The separation of the continents and the formation of seas at the beginning of the Jurassic led to climate change. Temperatures were somewhat cooler, rainfall somewhat higher. The resulting humidity led to a growth in luxuriant tropical vegetation with horsetails, ferns and ginkgoes. A large number of new dinosaur species appeared. In particular the large herbivores such as Brachiosaurus and Apatosaurus had plenty to eat and spread far and wide during the Jurassic era. Alongside them, the big carnivores such as Allosaurus evolved, together with smaller, lighter species such as the coelurosaurs. Flying reptiles dominated the skies. Archaeopteryx also appeared during the Jurassic.

During the Cretaceous, the continents drifted further apart, so that by the end of the period 65 million years ago, they were in much the same places as they are now. There were no longer many land bridges, and the dinosaur groups evolved independently of one another, so that new species sprung up on the different continents. All in all, there were more species during the Cretaceous than during the Triassic and Jurassic together. This makes it all the more mysterious why the creatures should have completely died out while in their heyday.

Family Tree

In order to compile a dinosaur family tree, we have to go back a little further in evolutionary history. The dinosaurs belong without a doubt in the group of Tetrapodes, in other words four-limbed vertebrates. These can be sub-divided into four classes: amphibians, reptiles, birds and mammals. Amphibians evolved from fish, and were the forerunners of the reptiles. From the reptiles, there evolved birds on the one hand, and mammals on the other.

Within the class of reptiles, there are four sub-classes, differing according to the arrangement of the temporal openings (or "fossae") at the side of the skull behind the eyes.

1. Anapsida: they have no temporal fossae;

2. Euryapsida: they have only one temporal fossa at the top (Nothosauria, Plesiosauria, Placodontia);

3. Synapsida: these mammal-like reptiles have only one temporal fossa at the bottom, with additional supports for stronger jaw muscles (Cynognathus);

4. Diapsida: they have two temporal fossae, one above and one below, separated by a piece of bone. The jaw muscles are connected by tendons that run through these openings. This means the jaws can be opened wider, and the owner can bite harder on its prey.

Our dinosaurs, like most modern reptiles, evolved from the Diapsida, as did

Bird-hipped dinosaur (Ornithischia)

the lords of the air, while the dinosaurs ruled the land, and the crocodiles, the only group still extant, conquered the seas and lakes. They developed from the oldest of the Archosauria, which peaked in the Triassic and were known as Thecodontia.

During this period the creatures started moving around in a different way. Gradually their limbs moved to take up a position immediately below their bodies. The "true" dinosaurs (alongside a group of early carnivorous saurians known as Herrerasauria) are sub-divided by the shape of their pelvis into two main groups: Ornithischia und Saurischia.

Every pelvis consists of three bones, the pubis, the ileum and the ischium. If the pubis and the ischium are fastened to the ileum in such a way that the pubis faces forwards and the ischium backwards, then we have a dinosaur from the Saurischia group (Greek: sauros = lizard, ischion = hip-joint). Sometimes these are known as "lizard-hipped" dinosaurs.

If the pubis and ischium are roughly parallel, facing backwards, as in modern birds, then we have a dinosaur of the Ornithischia variety

Development of skull forms among reptiles

Anapsida	tortoises and turtles
Euryapsida	marine reptiles, fish-saurians
Synapsida	mammal-like reptiles
Diapsida	dinosaurs, pterosaurs, crocodiles

the crocodiles and pterosaurs (flying reptiles).

Towards the end of the Permian, the Diapsida split into Lepidosauria and Archosauria. The evolution of the Lepidosauria led to 10,000 species of lizards and snakes. The Archosauria represent the reptiles that dominated the Earth for 180 million years. The pterosaurs were

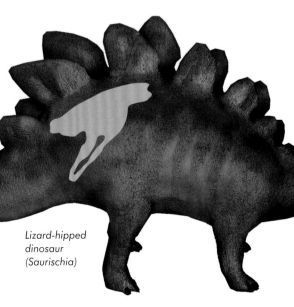

Lizard-hipped dinosaur (Saurischia)

(Greek: ornis, ornithos = bird). That's why they're also called "bird-hipped". Birds and Ornithischia do not have common ancestors, though.

During the course of their evolution, the Saurischia divided into the suborders Sauropodomorpha (huge herbivores such as Plateosaurus and Diplodocus) and Theropoda (carnivores such as Allosaurus, Deinonychus and Compsognathus).

The Ornithischia were all herbivores. They comprised four main groups, namely Ankylosauria (Ankylosaurus), Stegosauria (Kentrosaurus), Ceratopsia (Styracosaurus) and Ornithopoda (Echinodon, Edmontosaurus, Iguanodon, etc). A further common feature of all the Ornithischia was that their back teeth were enclosed by cheeks and turned slightly inwards. This gave the dinosaurs the ability to keep their food in their mouths while chewing it.

All dinosaurs walked on straight legs, and so did not have to creep like lizards or crocodiles.

Classification

After the term "dinosaur" was coined in 1841, numerous other dinosaur fossils were discovered. As a result, various systems of classification were proposed for these "new" species.

In 1887 the English anatomist Harry Seeley discovered that there were two basically different forms of pelvis in dinosaurs, as described above. These two orders were composed of suborders, to which the individual dinosaur families are assigned on the basis of various criteria, for example eating habits, method of locomotion, and size.

Likewise the other reptiles, such as pterosaurs, plesiosaurs, crocodiles etc., were also classified into their own orders with suborders and families.

Gallimimus

Theropoda

The Theropoda were a suborder of the Saurischia or lizard-hipped dinosaurs. Mostly they walked on two legs and ate meat. They can be sub-divided into two infra-orders:

1. Coelurosauria ("hollow-boned saurians"). These were mostly small, lightweight saurians. They get their name from the thin-walled hollow bones that made up most of their skeleton. Probably the largest Coelurosauria on dry land were the Tyrannosauridae, including that most popular of dinosaurs, Tyrannosaurus.

2. Carnosauria ("meat lizards"). These included many large, heavily-built predators and medium-sized carnivores.

The Coelurosauria comprised a number of families. Among the oldest are the Podokesauridae, which lived in the late Triassic and early Jurassic. They were still very similar to their direct ancestors, the Thecodonta, from which all the dinosaurs, pterosaurs and crocodiles were descended.

Another family, the Coeluridae, were active, fast-moving predators, whose slim bodies moved on two legs. They used their long tails for balance, and grabbed their prey with their front limbs, which were equipped with claws.

One side-branch of the Coelurosauria was the family of Ornithomimidae. These ostrich-like creatures (average length three metres) were toothless, long-legged sprinters. They included Gallimimus, the largest of the family at four metres.

The members of the Dromaeosauridae must have been particularly savage predators. They lived during the Cretaceous in North America and Asia. While they had the light build of the Coelurosauria, they also had the heavy skulls of the Carnosauria. This family included Deinonychus.

The Carnosauria were mostly powerful creatures with heavy bones.

Tyrannosaurus

They included a number of families. The largest carnivores of the Upper (late) Jurassic were the Allosauridae, which were only surpassed by Tyrannosaurus in the Cretaceous. The largest of the Allosauria was the one that gave the family its name, Allosaurus, with a length of 12 metres.

Somewhat earlier, from the Lower (early) Jurassic, there had been the family of the Megalosauridae. They had powerful bodies and heavy heads with numerous sharp teeth. This family included for example Megalosaurus.

One little feature distinguished the Ceratosauridae from the Megalosauridae: on their snouts they had a small horn or comb. Ceratosaurus was a member of this family.

Another family that probably developed from the Megalosauridae was that of the Spinosauridae. Their distinguishing feature was a sail or comb on their back, as can be seen on Spinosaurus.

Plateosaurus

Sauropodomorpha

The Sauropodomorpha belonged to the order of lizard-hipped saurians (Saurischia). They were herbivores that walked on all fours. Depending on size, they can be grouped into Prosauropoda and Sauropoda with their respective families. Although the Prosauropoda

Diplodocus

were once thought to be the ancestors of the Sauropoda, today they are believed to have been a side-branch. Their ancestors were probably also the ancestors of the Theropoda.

Probably the oldest of the Prosauropoda were the Anchisauridae. They resembled the somewhat larger Plateosauridae, of which Plateosaurus is doubtless the best-known member.

The Sauropoda included the families of the largest creatures ever to have walked the Earth. Externally they were characterized by a small head, a long neck, a large body with thick legs, and a long tail. Important families were the Brachiosauridae (Brachiosaurus), the Diplodocidae (Diplodocus, Apatosaurus, Mamenchisaurus) and the Camarasauriden

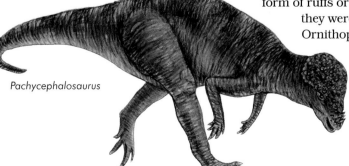

Pachycephalosaurus

(Camarasaurus). The last of the Sauropoda families was that of the Titanosauridae. They survived for some 80 million years until the end of the Cretaceous.

Ornithopoda

The Ornithopoda (the name means "bird-footed") were bird-hipped dinosaurs (Ornithischia). They were two-legged herbivores, mostly relatively small and nimble. They looked rather like the Coelurosauria, which were, however, Theropoda.

Heterodontosaurus

The Heterodontosauridae included Pisanosaurus and Heteroontosaurus.

The Pachycephalosauria were dinosaurs with massive roofs to their skulls. They were not so common. Apart from one exception (Yaverlandia) fossils have only been found in central Asia and North America. Apart from a domed skull, these saurians also had growths of bone at the backs and sides of their heads, or on their snouts, taking the form of ruffs or lumps. Otherwise, they were very like the Ornithopoda. A particularly large example was Pachycephalosaurus, which lived in the late Cretaceous.

Iguanodon

An important role was played by the family of Hypsilophontidae (Hypsilophodon). These creatures, reminiscent of modern gazelles, were found on all the continents. They were probably the ancestors of two groups, the Hadrosauria and the Iguanodons. The Hadrosauria, also known as duck-billed dinosaurs, had a whole variety of lumps and combs on their heads and backs. One common feature, though, was the broad, flattened snout, which ended in a toothless bill. Further back on their upper and lower jaws there were several rows of molars. This family included Corythosaurus, Parasaurolophus and Edmontosaurus.

The family of the Iguanodontidae was very widespread. Unlike their ancestors, the creatures had a clumsy build, so that they could not move very fast. Mostly they went on all fours, but they could also stand up on their hind legs. Iguanodon was the most famous member of the family.

Ankylosaurus

Ankylosauria

Another suborder of the Ornithischia (bird-hipped dinosaurs) was the Ankylosauria. These armoured creatures were more numerous at the end of the Cretaceous. They had heavily armoured heads, with heavy armour plating on their backs and tails too. These were covered in leathery skin and also spines and other protrusions.

This suborder comprised two families: the Nodosauridae and the Ankylosauridae. Little is known about the (older) Nodosauridae. We know they had small heads and armoured bodies. They must have had squat legs and broad feet to bear the heavy weight of the armour.

Among the chief features of the Ankylosauridae (Ankylosaurus) were the broad skull and a bony club at the end of the tail, allowing it to administer vicious sideswipes to its enemies.

Ceratopsia

The horned dinosaurs were a group of bird-hipped dinosaurs (Ornithischia) that first appeared in the Cretaceous.

These herbivores had armour only around their heads. Their ancestors included the family of the Psittacosauridae – the name means "parrot saurians". They could walk upright.

A typical example was Psittacosaurus from Asia. Likewise doubtless descended from the Psittacosauridae was the family of the Protoceratopsidae. These were primitive horned saurians that mostly walked on all fours. They didn't all have horns. On the whole, they were smaller than the later Ceratopsidae.

The family of the Ceratopsidae, which included Triceratops and Styracosaurus, was almost exclusively found in North America. These dinosaurs carried their massive bodies on four pillar-like legs. A conspicuous feature of these species was the neck shield, which came in various sizes, and the horns on their brow. Their sharp jaws were toothless.

Triceratops

Stegosauria

Another group of the Ornithischia (bird-hipped dinosaurs) was the Stegosauria. They had small heads and massive bodies with large horny plates rising from their backs. These mostly continued as spines along their tails right to the tip.

The Stegosauridae family had its heyday in the late Jurassic. They have been found in North America, Africa, Asia and Europe. In addition to Stegosaurus itself, of course, the family included Tuojiangosaurus and Kentrosaurus.

Stegosaurus

Pterosauria

The Pterosauria were the vultures of their age. They developed in the late Triassic and enjoyed a heyday in the Jurassic and early Cretaceous. They included the largest flying creatures the world has ever seen. Fossil finds have been made all over the world. Two suborders have been distinguished: the Rhamphorhynchoidae and the Pterodactyloidae. The former were the oldest of the flying saurians. They had relatively large heads, but the weight of the skull was reduced by temporal fossae. Their tails were quite long and consisted of ossified tendons, which made it stiff. A flying membrane was stretched across the neck and the long finger-bones, and was also attached to the thighs. This family included Eudimorphodon and Rhamphorhynchus.

Eudimorphodon

The family of Pterodactyloidae had a similar bodily structure to that of the Rhamphorhynchoidae. Mostly they had shorter tails, and some were flightless. The prime example of this group is the largest pterosaur, called Pteranodon.

Reptiles of the sea

The marine reptiles comprised four groups, which had adapted differently to life in the sea:

1. **Nothosauria**
2. **Placodontia**
3. **Plesiosauria**
4. **Ichthyosauria**

The **Nothosauria** comprised a number of families. The best-known is that of the Nothosauridae, including Nothosaurus, which gave the family its name. This creature led a similar life to present-day seals, in other words lived both on land and in the sea. It fed on fish.

The **Placodontia** also comprised a number of families. The Cyamodontidae, with an armoured back, resembled modern turtles. They lived from the Middle to Upper Triassic. The Henondontidae family looked even more like today's turtles. They had armoured backs and bellies, and a horny bill. They were found above all in the late Triassic.

The Placodontidae family lived in shallow-water zones, where they ate molluscs. Placodus was the typical example of this family.

The order **Plesiosauria** included two superfamilies, the Pliosauroidae and the Plesiosauroidae. Both comprised numerous sub-families which included individual species that grew to between 12 and 14 metres long. While the Plesiosauroidae, which included Elasmosaurus and Plesiosaurus, mostly lived on fish, the Pliosauridae hunted sharks and ichthyosaurs.

The **Ichthyosauria** were adapted most fully to a marine lifestyle. They gave birth to their young in the sea. Their bodies no longer allowed them on to dry land, for they were similar in build to present-day dolphins.

Among the families belonging to the order Ichthyosauria were the Mixosauridae (Mixosaurus), the Ichthyosauridae (Ichthyosaurus) and the Leptopterygiidae, which were among the last of the "fish-lizards".

Nothosaurus

Early Diapsida

Most modern reptiles belong to the sub-class Diapsida. The early diapsids were the precursors of our modern lizards and snakes. The extinct pterosaurs and dinosaurs were also descended from them.

Elasmosaurus

One of the most primitive orders of Diapsida comprised the Araeoscelida. They looked like long-necked lizards with spindly legs. One

Araeoscelis

member of this order was Araeoscelis, a small creature 60 centimetres long, which lived during the Permian.

There were many more orders, including the Thalattosauria, Eosuchia and Sphenodonta. One living member of the Sphenodonta is the tuatara, a lizard still found in New Zealand.

Early Archosaurs/ Crocodiles

One large group of "dominant" reptiles was the Archosauria, which comprised four orders, the Ornithischia, the Saurischia, the Pterosauria and the Crocodyla. The archosaurs had developed from the Thecodontia, which lived in the Upper Permian. Their heyday was the Triassic period, at the end of which they became extinct. The Thecodontia were reptiles that resembled lizards and crocodiles, and they had one feature in common: every tooth grew out of its own hollow in the jaw, and not directly out of the surface of the jawbone. It was this that distinguished the Thecodontia from all other reptiles of that time.

The Thecodontia comprised a number of suborders. The oldest of theses groups was the Proterusuchia, from which the other groups were probably descended.

The suborder Phytosauria were crocodile-like Thecodontia that lived in the water. The suborder Rauisuchia included carnivores that lived on dry land. Their hind limbs were already positioned further beneath their bodies than was the case with the Proterusuchia. Herbivorous Thecodontia belonged to the suborder Aetosauria, which lived in the late Triassic.

The suborder Ornithosuchia is regarded by scientists as representing the link between the four-legged Thecodontia and the two-legged dinosaurs. The group that most resembled the dinosaurs was the Lagosuchidae family,

Lagosuchus

represented by Lagosuchus. Some experts even regard these as the ancestors of the pterosaurs.

Doubtless the most successful of the Archosauria were the crocodiles. They probably developed from the Ornithosuchia, and they are the only ones to have survived to this day. One example of an early crocodile was Protosuchus. It lived in North America in the early Jurassic and was very similar to our present-day crocodiles.

Dimetrodon

Pelycosauria/ Therapsida

The oldest mammal-like reptiles were the Pelycosauria. These can be divided into the Ophiacodontidae, Edaphosauridae and Sphenacodontidae families, of which the more highly developed Therapsida were presumably a side-branch. They all had one thing in common: their synapsidal skull with its large opening behind the eye-sockets allowed the development of long jawmuscles. This made it possible for the creatures to bite harder and open their mouths wider.

The Pelycosauria order included. Dimetrodon, Ophiacodon and Edaphosaurus.

The Therapsida probably split off as long ago as the early Permian, but fossil finds date only from the late Permian. They include the carnivorous reptiles Titanosuchus and Lycaenops. Cynognathus was a member of another group of therapsids, the Cynodontia. These creatures were around for a particularly long time, namely 80 million years (from the late Permian to the middle Jurassic). They are among the direct ancestors of the mammals.

Protosuchus

Cynognathus

Family Life

As a result of numerous fossil discoveries, we have some insight into the family lives of the dinosaurs. One find in south-western Mongolia in the 1920s was particularly interesting. The nests and eggs of a small horned dinosaur (Protoceratops) were discovered in a hollow. Up to 20 relatively long oval eggs were arranged in a circle. Beside them were several skeletons of the creatures. Probably the mother had dug a kind of pit in which she squatted to lay one egg after another. The eggs were lightly covered with sand. Either the sand was warmed by the sun, or else the air temperature was sufficient to hatch the eggs.

One thing is certain though: the dinosaur mother did not brood these eggs herself. In Montana, a number of nests have been found containing eggs: these were covered with pieces of plant, as if in a compost heap. The eggs themselves were intact, apart from the hole made by the baby dinosaur as it hatched. This suggests that these dinosaurs could walk as soon as they hatched and follow their mother the way chicks follow a hen. The fact that skeletons of young dinosaurs were also found nearby suggests that while they left the nest, they did not wander far afield at first.

Elsewhere nests have been found containing fossilized young. In this case, the young dinosaurs remained in the nest while they were fed by their mother. Crushed eggshells found in the same nest support this theory. Probably the parents died while foraging for food, leaving the young to starve because they waited in the nest for the adult creatures to return.

Numerous finds indicate that many dinosaurs lived in herds. They formed veritable breeding colonies, enabling them to keep watch on one another's nests. The largest eggs ever found were laid, incidentally, by the sauropods or giant herbivores. A single egg weighed seven kilograms.

Extinction

Rock from the Cretaceous period

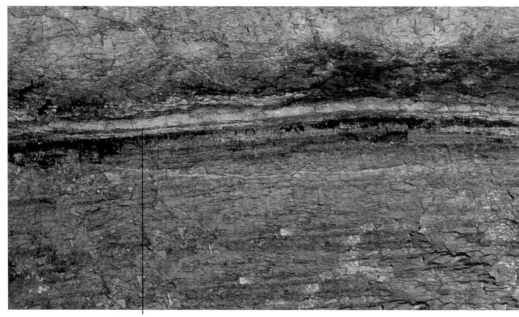

Iridium layer

Scientists are still not sure why the dinosaurs died out more than 65 million years ago. Other plants and animals died out at the same time, while many species survived. The species that disappeared include marine reptiles such as the plesiosaurs and ichthyosaurs, as well as those crocodiles that lived in the sea. Freshwater crocodiles by contrast were spared. The flying saurians disappeared, but birds lived on. Among other creatures to survive were tortoises and turtles, frogs, and mammals.

But back to the dinosaurs. While the fossils tell us when particular species were more abundant, they don't tell us whether it took a million years for the dinosaurs to finally

Meteorite impact

become extinct, or whether this happened suddenly. Various theories have been proposed over the years. One not very convincing idea is that the dinosaurs reproduced so successfully that the result was overpopulation, leading to constant stress, which in turn led to a failure of reproduction.

Nor can the dinosaurs have been wiped out by epidemics. There were so many different species on such different continents that they couldn't all have died out. Nor does anyone still believe that the dinosaurs ate each other out of existence, i.e. that the carnivores ate the herbivores and starved because there were no more to eat.

Another theory maintains that over the course of time new plants evolved which contained poisons lethal to dinosaurs. Some scientists think that there were particular climate changes 65 million years ago. Seasonal variations, they say, replaced the previous evenly warm temperatures.

One widely accepted theory holds that the dinosaurs were wiped out by the impact of an asteroid or meteorite. This view is based on the discovery of relatively large quantities of iridium in a layer of rocks 65 million years old. This element is extremely rare on Earth, but it is more frequent in meteoric dust.

In the opinion of the scientists, this huge meteorite or asteroid, which must have been at least ten kilometres in diameter, threw up such a vast cloud of dust that for several years no sunlight could get through to the Earth's surface. As a result, plant growth ceased and plant-eaters starved. In addition, the Earth grew cold, so that the creatures froze to death.

Once the dust clouds settled, it became very hot, because the water-vapour produced by the meteorite produced a greenhouse effect. The resulting heat killed off the remaining dinosaurs, which were not adapted to live in such conditions.

It has been found that the Cretaceous was a period of unusual volcanic activity; for millions of years, masses of lava were produced by the eruptions. In some cases, the iridium mentioned above was spewed out in particularly high concentrations.

Among the places most affected were the western United States, Greenland, parts of Britain, but especially India. Here, in the Deccan Traps, in sediments enclosed in lava masses, the nest colonies and eggs of the final representatives of Titanosaurus (sauropods living in Gondwana) have been found.

But whatever the cause of their disappearance in the flesh, the dinosaurs live on in the interest of mankind.

Fossilization

"Fossils" is the name given to the preserved remains of plants or animals that existed in the Earth's past. These fossils may be bones, footprints, or shells, or else impressions of leaves or other soft items. In order for these remains to have been preserved, in other words fossilized, certain conditions were necessary. First, the dead creature must have been rapidly embedded in an environment where it could not be eaten. Then it must be excluded as far as possible from contact with the air, in order to slow down decomposition. Wind and water can also have a destructive effect on a corpse.

So how does fossilization come about? In the most favourable scenario, a plant or animal is covered by sand immediately after death, for example on the beach or in a desert. The flowing lava of a volcano has a similar effect. Or else they might sink to the bottom of a river or lake. Or they could be deep-frozen. In all these cases, the dead organism is covered by sediments that gradually build up. Now decomposition processes set in: muscles, skin, cartilage etc. can dissolve when covered in water, for example.

Ichthyosaurus: fossil from the Swabian Jura near Holzminden, Germany

Trilobite: fossil dating from the Cambrian period

The main components of bone, protein and mineral substances, also decompose, resulting in a hollow space that leaves a "negative impression" of the bone.

Sometimes the natural components of the bone are replaced by mineral substances in the water, so that the final result is a bone that has literally turned to stone. The best conditions, however, are no water, no air. When the organism is covered in sand, clay or other air-tight substances, the hard components gradually turn to stone.

Because they are continually being overlaid by sediments, and also because of movements of the Earth's crust, fossils can remain hidden for millions of years until finally, other movements of the Earth's crust, or maybe erosion, uncover them once more.

Since every sedimentary layer can be dated to a particular period of the Earth's history, it is also possible to use fossils to find out which creatures were alive during a particular period. The history of the dinosaurs began in the Earth's middle era, known as the Mesozoic. Fossils have been found in layers of rocks to prove this. The same goes for plant fossils.

Other layers of rocks provide the evidence that the dinosaurs died out suddenly. From one layer to the next, all the species disappear entirely.

The Earth's Infancy

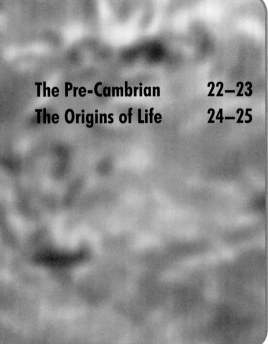

Very little is known about the Hadean and Archean eons, the first 2 billion years after the Earth was born. Nor is there complete certainty about how the Earth was formed. Either the planetary system – and hence our Earth – split off from the sun, or else it formed by the aggregation of cosmic particles.

After the sun had condensed in space at enormous temperatures in the universe, it began to cool down. The condensation of further materials whirling around into gas, ice and radioactive particles led to the formation of more celestial bodies (planetoids), which, through the force of gravity, attracted more and more particles until finally they became planets orbiting the sun. It is thought that the universe was already ten billion years old when the sun and proto-planets formed.

The process by which the formation of the planets and their moons took place is believed to have been completed some five billion years ago. The Hadean eon began 4.6 billion years ago. After the Earth's globe had been formed, it slowly cooled down, as did the atmosphere. Water formed, which in turn evaporated before falling back on the Earth's still cooling surface as the primordial rain. As a result, existing rocks were broken up and the first sedimentary rocks were formed. There was still no oxygen in the atmosphere for animals or plants. Consequently there was no life. From the period of the Earth's formation, and then the Hadean and Archeon eons, we now move on to the Pre-Cambrian.

The Pre-Cambrian

The Pre-Cambrian, also known as the Eozoic era, comprises most of the Earth's history, namely about nine-tenths of it. Within this immense time-span of four billion years, the seas and continents formed, as well as an atmosphere which provided the pre-conditions in which life could form.

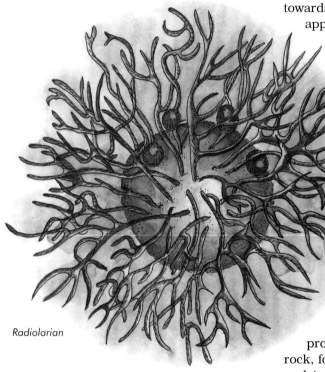

Radiolarian

In recent decades, rocks have been found in various parts of the world which the latest calculations and close examinations have dated to 4 billion years old. The oldest come from sediments in Canada, South Africa and Greenland. There are very few fossil organisms as old as this, and most of them are plants.

In the oldest rocks, what we find are first and foremost threadlike and globular micro-organisms such as single-celled cyanobacteria (sometimes known as blue-green algae), while the younger rocks already have branching cyanobacteria and primitive fungi. These have been found in limestone deposits in Ontario and in rocks in Minnesota and Britain.

Animal fossils are very infrequent in the Pre-Cambrian. Probably only towards the end of this era did any appear at all, and they were largely jellyfish, Annelida (segmented worms) and Radiolaria (plankton). As these creatures have no hard parts, they do not fossilize easily, and hence there are not many fossils. It was not until the Cambrian period that organisms with hard parts occur in any numbers, so that from this time on fossil finds become more frequent. All the continental regions of the Pre-Cambrian must have been empty and barren. There were probably huge masses of bare rock, for the life that was gradually evolving was developing in the shallow seas. The single-celled organisms without a nucleus (Prokaryotes) nourished themselves from the "primordial soup" and only released small quantities of oxygen when generating energy; but now, with the appearance of organic substances like chlorophyll, oxygen production was greatly increased. Gradually the oxygen content grew under the influence of sunlight. It also increased in the atmosphere, so that soon a protective ozone layer formed, which held back the destructive ultra-violet radiation of the sun. Beneath this

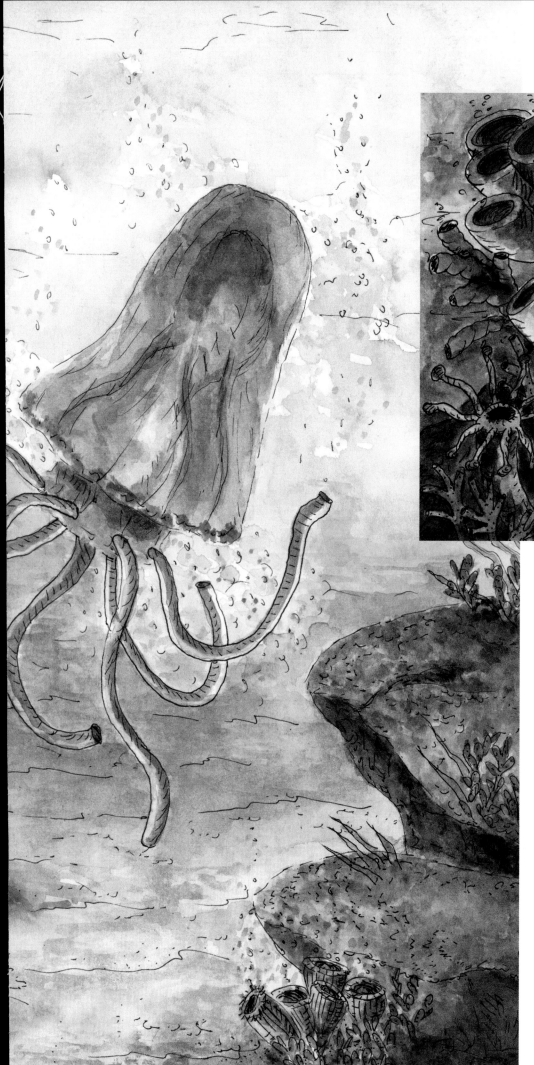

protective layer, it was possible for a living world to develop on Earth. It is presumed that temperatures were in the range from 0 to 50 degrees Celsius, because only in these conditions is it possible for life to evolve.

Maybe there were also widespread glaciations during this period. The Earth was never entirely covered in ice, however. From the start of the Cambrian, a wide variety of primitive species developed in the sea, as numerous fossils prove.

By the end of the Pre-Cambrian flora and fauna had already colonized the sea-bed in large numbers. However, these organisms were still very simple in structure. Alongside algae, which represented the plant kingdom, there were various species of sponges, polyps and jellyfish. Sponges actually consist of an empty space enclosed in a double layer of cells. Polyps and jellyfish have more specialized cells. In the course of their lives, polyps develop stationary forms, while jellyfish can float freely.

23

The Origins of Life

Where does life come from? Where on earth did it first appear? In what sea and on what continent did the first living cells develop? These are questions that we shall probably never be able to answer.

Our Earth originated around 4.6 billion years ago. Even today, no one knows for sure what planted the seeds of life on Earth. Given the prevailing conditions at the time, life should not have been possible.

The atmosphere contained no oxygen, but poisonous gases, while strong ultra-violet radiation beat down upon the Earth. Electric storms raged continually, and there were constant volcanic eruptions. The Earth's land surface was unstable and in constant motion. And yet there was one safe habitat: the water.

Probably it was there, 3.8 billion years ago, that the first signs of life appeared as the ocean waves gradually calmed. The earliest evidence is provided by rocks with microscopic particles which may be the remains of bacteria-like organisms.

During this time, chemical reactions began, and at some time or other beneath the warmth of the sun in the primordial soup there developed chains of molecules, about whose reproduction we still know very little.

The first single-celled organisms appeared. They are known as prokaryotes, and they are still around today. They included bacteria and cyanobacteria. Their cells still had no nucleus. In rocks 3.5 billion years old, a particular kind of layered limestone sediments has been found, known as stromatolites, which may well have been excreted by cyanobacteria in shallow waters.

For almost two billion years this was the only kind of single-celled organism. Some of the early cells finally succeeded in producing chlorophyll. This made photosynthesis possible, of which oxygen is a by-product. This oxygen escaped into the atmosphere.

Exposed to strong sunlight, some of this oxygen gradually turned to ozone, a gas that wards off most of the radiation from space. Once the atmosphere contained oxygen, it was possible, 1.5 billion years ago, for highly developed cells to evolve, with a nucleus and a membrane.

About 680 million years ago, the single-celled organisms developed into multicellular life-forms. Following marine algae, the first marine animals evolved: jellyfish. This happened about 600 million years ago.

The first animals with a hard external skeleton formed in the Cambrian between 510 and 570 million years ago. In the Ordovician period, the first land plants evolved, with a leafy skin to prevent the rapid evaporation of water. The first amphibians emerged from the water 365 million years ago. To lay their eggs, though, they needed the security of the water.

With the first reptiles 340 million years ago, dry land was colonized for the first time. Their particular skin-structure (scales protected it from drying out), and the fact that their eggs were enclosed in shells (enabling them to store their own water-supply), made them independent of the water.

First cells 3.8 billion years ago

First bony fish 410 million years ago

In the millions of years that followed, numerous kinds of reptiles evolved on dry land, including the dinosaurs. Other reptiles lived in the sea or in the air. When the dinosaurs died out 65 million years ago, the mammals, small at first, were able to develop in great diversity. Huge whales swam around in the seas, while birds had taken to the air.

We have a large quantity of fossil evidence from this period to prove the existence of animal species now long-extinct. This is how we know that many creatures, whether mammals, reptiles, birds or insects, were very similar to present-day forms.

Humans, which now dominate the Earth, did not evolve until a few million years ago. And although this period represents only a fraction of the Earth's total history, they have already brought about decisive changes that are disturbing the equilibrium of the planet.

First reptiles 340 million years ago

First dinosaurs 230 million years ago

In the course of geological time, organisms have become more mobile and more complex. Almost 4 billion years ago, the first cells evolved. These developed into ever more complex multicellular organisms, and ultimately the vertebrates. Fish evolved limbs about 400 million years ago, which allowed them to crawl on to dry land. As a next step, they could, as reptiles, live entirely independently of the water. They had their heyday in the Mesozoic era, when, as dinosaurs, they colonized almost the entire world. When they died out, mammals gradually replaced them.

The Palaeozoic Era

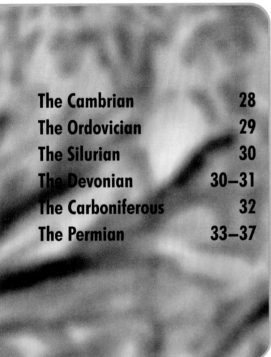

The Palaeozoic Era (the name comes from the Greek for "ancient animals") was the time between the Pre-Cambrian and the Mesozoic ("middle animals"), and lasted about 320 million years. It is sub-divided into a number of "periods": Cambrian, Ordovician, Silurian, Devonian, Carboniferous and Permian. Unlike the Pre-Cambrian, these periods were characterized by numerous plant and animal species. Alongside corals, trilobites and placoderms (armoured fish), there also developed a wide variety of brachiopods, cephalopods (Nautiloidea) and graptolites.

During the Devonian there were also coelacanths and amphibians. Later, sea-urchins and more advanced fish developed. Spiders, millipedes and insects likewise appeared during this period. The Permian saw the appearance of the first primitive reptiles, including Dimetrodon, a carnivore, and Edaphosaurus, a herbivore. Other reptiles, the Pelycosauria and Therapsida, looked quite different. They were already mammal-like. They included Ophiacodon and Titanosuchus. However there were still no tortoises or turtles, birds or mammals.

As for the world of plants, this was the heyday of marine flora, and the Devonian also saw the first land-based plants such as ferns and club-mosses. During the Carboniferous period, these evolved into trees, which formed huge swampy forests (our present-day coalfields). These were largely replaced by primitive conifers in the late Permian.

The Cambrian

The Cambrian is the earliest period of the Palaeozoic era. It takes its name from the name the Romans gave to North Wales, "Cambria", where rocks of this period have been found.

During this period, in other words 600 million years ago, all the primordial continents were separated once more before drifting back at the start of the Triassic period to form the supercontinent called Pangaea. This is proved by palaeomagnetic measurements. In the southern hemisphere there was basically one large land mass, which later became Gondwana. This was divided by a broad oceanic belt from the various land masses in the northern hemisphere, which were divided by seas from each other. They later formed Laurasia.

It is believed that the North Pole at the time was in what is now the north-western Pacific. The South Pole probably lay in what is now north-west Africa. The climate was cool to temperate to start with, but later global warming set in, as indicated by scientific investigations of red sandstones and sediments such as salt and gypsum.

Eurypterid (sea scorpion) fossil

Trilobite

The Cambrian saw a rapid explosion of plant and animal life. A wide variety of trilobites and crustaceans with hard external skeletons of chitin developed in the seas. There were also early molluscs. These species lived on the sea-bed, while jellyfish and sponges floated in the water. The world of plants consisted mainly of various algae and seaweeds. There were still no land plants or land animals. They only developed later.

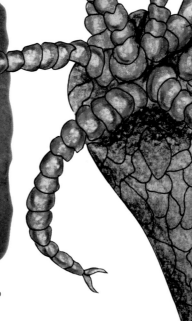

Horseshoe crab (arthropod)

The Ordovician

Ordovician (510–439 million years ago)

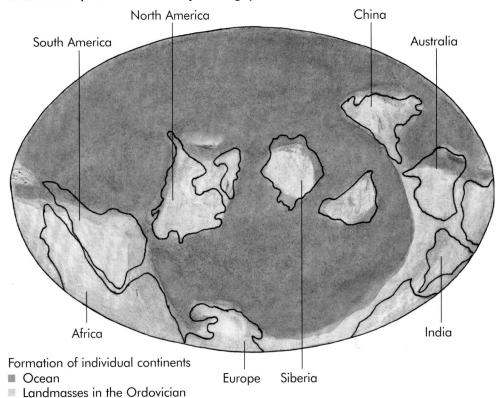

Formation of individual continents
■ Ocean
▨ Landmasses in the Ordovician

The Ordovician is the period of the Palaeozoic era following on from the Cambrian. It was named after a Celtic tribe, the Ordovices, that lived in North Wales. It lasted from 510 to 439 million years ago. The Earth's geography was much like that in the Cambrian; the continents were moving towards each other, while their coastal regions were increasingly flooded.

During the Ordovician, there was an ice age. The boulders pushed together by the glaciers can be identified today as sediments in South America. Because the seas were the dominant feature, this was where the animal world in particular developed. As sediments in black shales demonstrate, multicellular graptolites were the predominant life-form in the deeper waters: these were an extinct form of hemichordate with a chitin-like external skeleton; they formed colonies.

In the shallow seas, numerous kinds of trilobite were the dominant life-form in the sandy limestone sediments. These were arthropods, and their bodies had armour-plated backs consisting of three jointed sections: a head shield (comprising a central section and two lateral sections), a rump (mostly consisting of a number of movable segments) and a short tail section (also segmented). This extinct class, of which there were more than 1,500 genera (100,000 species) lived mainly on animal and plant remains.

In the fossilized sandy deserts of the Ordovician period, the fossilized remains of the sort of trail that a millipede might leave have been discovered. If such a species did exist on land, there must also have been land plants at this time for it to live off.

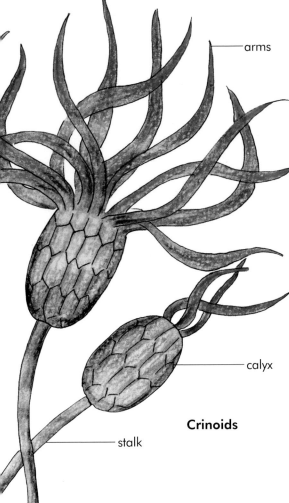

Crinoids

arms

calyx

stalk

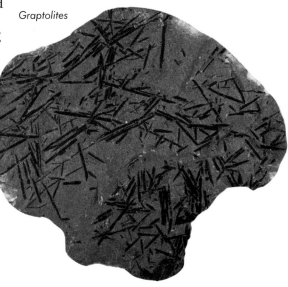

Graptolites

29

The Silurian

The Silurian was the third period of the Palaeozoic era. It was named after a pre-Celtic tribe, the Silures, who lived in Wales. The period occupied the time between 438 and 408 million years ago. Geographically, there were two largely self-contained continents, Laurasia in the north and Gondwana in the south. These were flooded to a greater or lesser extent.

The North Pole at the time is thought to have been in today's northern Pacific, while the South Pole was in south-western Africa. The Equator ran from south-eastern

Fossil starfish

Crinoids and feather stars (Clematocrinus retiarius)

ocean habitat. They included first and foremost graptolites (extinct hemichordates with a chitin-like outer skeleton) in the deep waters, and trilobites (arthropods) and simple corals in the shallows.

The corals, which built up huge reefs at the time and still exert a fascination on scientists, died out about 230 million years ago, and were replaced by the modern corals that can be found in today's warm oceans.

Lituites lituus (cephalopod)

Europe to northern Australia, Greenland and the middle of North America.

The climate was mostly warm and humid, but grew somewhat drier towards the end of the period. This is indicated by the sandstones, gypsum and salts that date from this era. Marine invertebrates were among the chief denizens of the

Sea-scorpions, also arthropods, attained huge dimensions of up to two metres in length (Pterygotus). Feather stars, which had already been around in the Ordovician, became widespread. They consisted of parts arranged like a star around a centre. Each of their five arms had several dozen suckers.

The first jawless fish appeared in the seas. They had no bones, but a skeleton of cartilage. We only know of their existence because they had small bony plates on their heads and bodies, and it was these that fossilized. Of the boneless fish, only the eel-like lampreys and the wormlike blennies have survived to the present. Echinoderms, which alongside algae were also enjoying a heyday, were animals consisting of a chalice-like body anchored by a stalk to the sea-bed. Their body was surrounded by numerous tentacles. Meanwhile towards the end of the Silurian, the first primordial ferns and club-mosses developed.

Starfish

Trilobite (arthropod)

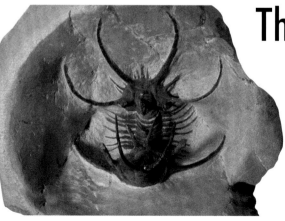

The Devonian

The fourth period of the Palaeozoic era, named after the county of Devon in England, lasted from 409 to 363 million years ago. At this time too, the continents were in constant motion. The climate in the northern hemisphere was warm, but there are signs of glaciation in

the area of the South Pole.

After their beginnings in the Ordovician, land plants now developed numerous species, in particular horsetails, Psilophytales and ferns, which during the later Devonian also grew as trees.

Things were happening in the animal world, too. Those species that lived in the water developed apace, indeed the Devonian is known as the Age of Fish. From the jawless fish there developed the armoured fish, the first vertebrates to have jaws. To start with, the skeletons of the first vertebrates consisted not of bone, but of cartilage. The foreparts of the armoured fish were encased in bony armour, while the rear parts were covered in scales. They grew up to eight metres long, enjoying a heyday during the Devonian, before dying out towards the end of the period.

The cartilaginous fish include today's dominant marine predators, the sharks, as well as skates and rays. Not much is known of their evolutionary history, because only their teeth fossilized, while the cartilaginous skeletons dissolved.

The first bony fish were the coelacanths, which largely breathed through lungs, and had thick fins

Devonian (409–363 million years ago)

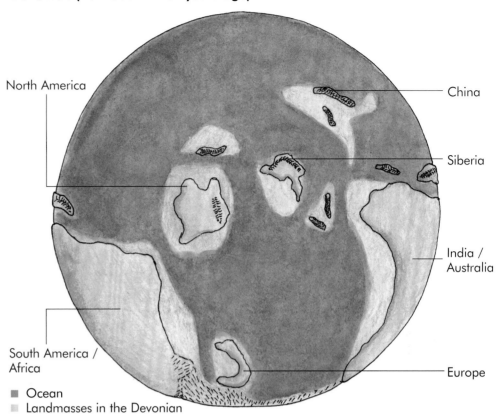

North America — China — Siberia — India / Australia — South America / Africa — Europe

■ Ocean
▨ Landmasses in the Devonian

with a firm bony frame. They dominated the waters of the Devonian. They were thought to have long since died out, until in 1938 a live coelacanth was caught off the east coast of South Africa. Since then, a number have been found. These modern coelacanths, however, breathe not through lungs but through gills, like the ray-finned fish, which include most modern fish and were already also present in the Devonian. We know that the ancient coelacanths were able to use their muscular fins to move about on land, which would have allowed them to leave a dried-up lake or river to find another with water in it.

Another group of bony fish were the lungfish, of which very few species are still extant. They also lived in rivers and lakes that periodically

Shark

In the Devonian, also known as the Age of Fish, the first sharks appeared. Even today they are the dominant predators of the oceans.

dried out, but during the dry phases they could bury themselves in mud and there survive the drought through their ability to breathe through lungs. Their young, however, were totally dependent on water. Later, they developed the ability to live on land: the first amphibians were born.

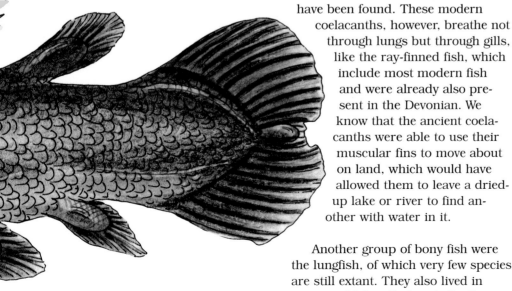

Coelacanth

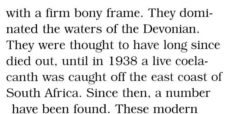

The Carboniferous

Carboniferous (363–290 million years ago)

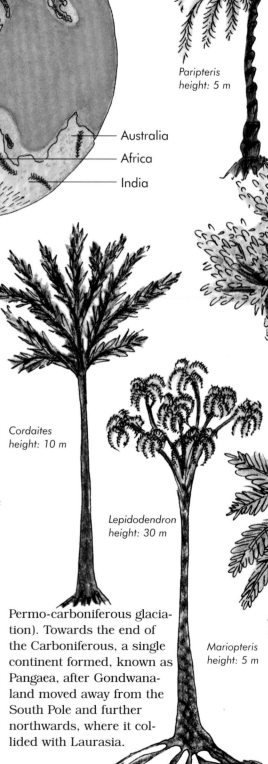

North America — Siberia

China

South America

Australia

Africa

India

■ Ocean
■ Land masses in the Carboniferous
■ Orogeny
□ Glacier

*Paripteris
height: 5 m*

*Cordaites
height: 10 m*

*Lepidodendron
height: 30 m*

*Mariopteris
height: 5 m*

The Carboniferous, whose name comes from the Latin word for coal, was the fifth geological period of the Palaeozoic era. It lasted from 363 to 290 million years ago, and is also known as the Age of Coal, for it was then that the largest coalfields in the Earth's history were formed. The climate in central Europe, which at the time lay close to the Equator, was tropically hot and humid, like the Amazon rain forest today.

The Carboniferous was a period of increased activity in the Earth's crust. These movements of the tectonic plates created mountain ranges, inter-sected by valleys. Vast forests grew along the coasts, which were periodi-cally flooded, only to grow once more when the sea-level dropped. In these areas, which were located primarily in Europe and North America, extensive coalfields formed. These were like today's tropical marshy forests, except that there were neither birds nor flowering plants.

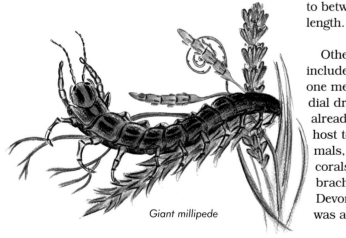

Giant millipede

Trees with bark grew to heights of 30 metres, but they had only a small solid wooden core, which easily broke. It was in this environment that the first land-based vertebrates (amphibians and reptiles) developed. Amphibians, such as the armoured

Diplocaulus, evolved from the transi-tional forms between fish and land-based vertebrates (Ichthyostega). Like today's amphibians, they lived close to water, where they also deposited their eggs in the form of spawn. They grew to between two and three metres in length.

Other denizens of the Carboniferous included giant millipedes that grew to one metre in length, spiders, primor-dial dragonflies and other insects. As already in the Devonian, the seas were host to unicellular plants and ani-mals, numerous algae, but also corals, trilobites, cephalopods and brachiopods or lampshells. As in the Devonian, the number of fish species was also very large.

In the southern hemisphere, Gond-wana was still one large continent con-sisting of North America, India, Africa, Australia and Antarctica. A large part of this land mass was close to what was then the South Pole, and in the transition to the Permian period was covered in huge masses of ice (the

Permo-carboniferous glacia-tion). Towards the end of the Carboniferous, a single continent formed, known as Pangaea, after Gondwana-land moved away from the South Pole and further northwards, where it col-lided with Laurasia.

The Permian

The final geological period of the Palaeozoic era was the Permian. It lasted from about 290 to 245 million years ago, and was named after the Russian region of Perm, to the west of the Urals.

During this period, Gondwana collided with the northern continents to form the huge land mass of Pangaea, which led to considerable mountain formation through folding of the Earth's crust. This supercontinent was surrounded by one large ocean, Panthalassa. Here, corals, ammonites and large single-celled organisms continued to exist.

Brachiopods developed coral-like into large formations, as did various molluscs. Many of these species died out at the end of the Permian. The cause is unknown. It may have been due to the gradual retreat of the seas. Some of the armoured amphibians remained in the vicinity of the water, and grew even bigger. Others gradually moved further away from the water. These developed into a huge variety of reptiles. Smaller specimens, like our modern frogs, could feed on insects while on land, but for larger amphibians, this was insufficient.

It is difficult in the case of many creatures of this period to decide whether they were still amphibians or already reptiles. Many of them now laid their eggs on dry land, where they could be hatched by the heat of the sun.

The joining of Laurasia and Gondwana allowed early amphibians and reptiles to advance into Gondwana too, where they had not previously occurred. The so-called comb-lizards that appeared in the Permian were already genuine reptiles. They included Dimetrodon and Edaphosaurus. Also present were Titanosuchus, a more highly developed reptile, and Lycaenops, an ancestor of the mammals.

The flora of the Permian was characterized by the advance of conifers and a retreat of trees with bark.

Titanosuchus

Titanosuchus was already among the more highly developed synapsid reptiles of the Permian period. It has been found in parts of Africa. At 2.50 metres long, Titanosuchus had a crocodile-like body with a conspicuously large skull up to one metre long.

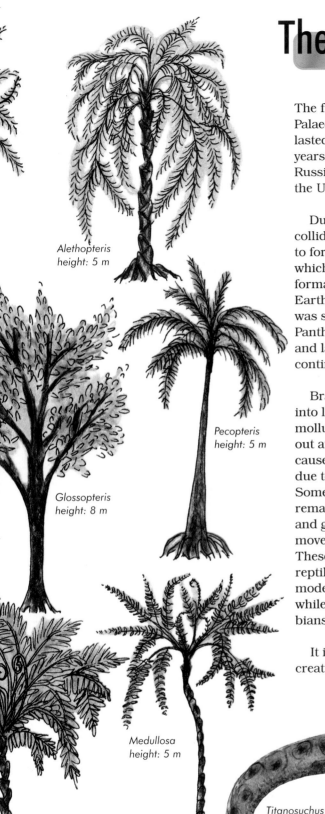

Alethopteris
height: 5 m

Pecopteris
height: 5 m

Glossopteris
height: 8 m

Medullosa
height: 5 m

Plants of the Carboniferous and Permian

Titanosuchus
Mammal-like reptile

Order: Therapsida

A large opening in the skull behind the eye-sockets made it possible to develop long jaw muscles, which in turn allowed the creature to open its jaws wide and close them powerfully. Titanosuchus was a predatory beast, which presumably lived on plant-eating reptiles. This is indicated by its sharp incisors, the long pointed canine teeth, and the fact that the back teeth were adapted to tearing.

Ophiacodon
Mammal-like reptile

Order: Pelycosauria

Ophiacodon

The dominant animals of the Permian period were the Parareptilia and the mammal-like reptiles. The latter group included Ophiacodon. It lived on the banks of ponds and rivers in North America and weighed in at an estimated 30 to 50 kilograms, with a length of 3.5 metres.

Unlike the other mammal ancestors Edaphosaurus and Dimetrodon, Ophiacodon did not have a sail of skin on its back. It must have regulated its body temperature some other way. This was probably done by means of a particularly fast metabolic rate.

By looking at Ophiacodon, we can see how the mammal-like reptiles developed. The skull had already become long in shape, so that long jaw muscles could form, allowing the creature to open its mouth wide.

Its eyes lay somewhat to the side, so that it had a relatively broad field of vision. If Ophiacodon lay in wait in shallow water or on the bank, it could keep quite still and yet keep watch for passing prey, which consisted chiefly of fish. It would hold its mouth wide open and then snap it shut, retiring to enjoy its meal in peace and quiet.

Ophiacodon could both swim and move well on land. Its legs were already positioned somewhat beneath its body, allowing the typical crawling gait of the reptiles to evolve into something more like running, which was faster.

Araeoscelis

One of the early reptiles of the Permian was Araeoscelis. This creature, which lived in North America, looked rather like a lizard, with its long, thin legs, its long neck, and a long tail.

It was only about 60 centimetres long altogether, and had a very small head. Its teeth were broad and blunt, but tapering. This would have allowed it to open, without difficulty, the hard exo-skeltons of the beetles that formed its staple diet.

Araeoscelis belonged to the sub-class Diapsida. These animals were characterized by two openings (fossae) in the skull, covered with skin, behind each eye-socket. In Araeoscelis, one of these fossae had been filled in with bone once more. This made its skull stronger, and allowed it to bite harder.

The early Diapsida were the ancestors not only of most of our present-day reptiles, including the crocodiles, but also of the extinct dinosaurs and pterosaurs.

Pareiasaurus
Early primitive reptile

Suborder: Parareptilia
Order: Pareiasauria

Araeoscelis

Subclass: Diapsida
Order: Araeoscelida

Pareiasaurus

One of the largest of the parareptiles was the Pareiasaur. Its relatives were distributed all over the world, but particularly in southern Europe, and in parts of Africa. A well-preserved skeleton was discovered in the more than 250-million-year-old Permian sediments in the Karoo desert in South Africa.

Pareiasaurus had a massive body up to 2.5 metres long. The heavy skull looked very strange, with its numerous bony growths, especially in the lower section. There were still no hollows to save weight. Its numerous teeth were simple and leaf-like. They allowed the creature to chew up the plants that grew on the river banks.

The limbs of Pareiasaurus were very thick, with broad feet to allow it to keep its balance. They were positioned further below its torso than was the case in earlier reptiles, allowing it to walk rather than crawl.

Dimetrodon

One of the ancestors of the mammal-like reptiles (Pelycosauria) was Dimetrodon. This was a huge lizard about three metres long, with a long tail.

Dimetrodon had a large sail on its back, supported by spiky outcrops of the vertebrae. This "sail" could be raised to a height of up to a metre. It was well supplied with blood-vessels, and served to regulate body temperature. In the morning, Dimetrodon would raise its sail towards the sun, and thus absorb heat. Scientists have calculated that if it weighed 200 kilograms, without the sail it would have taken 200 minutes to get its temperature from 26° to 32° Celsius. The sail reduced the time to just 80 minutes.

Dimetrodon needed to raise its temperature in order to make an early start hunting, while its rivals were still sluggish because of the cold. Conversely, the sail could also be used to radiate excess heat, which the creature did by raising it in the shade. This sail was probably a first step to warm-bloodedness, which only evolved during the Triassic.

Its preferred prey included reptile-like amphibians such as Diadectes, a peaceful herbivore up to three metres long. There were many of these and similar species on the shores of the large lakes and the adjacent tree-fern forests. Dimetrodon lived in parts of North America and Europe.

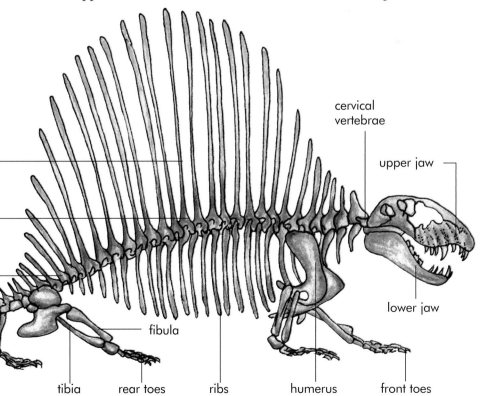

**Dimetrodon skeleton
Synapsid skull**

vertebral spikes up to 1 m long

thoracic vertebrae

lumbar vertebrae

caudal vertebrae

tibia

rear toes

fibula

ribs

humerus

front toes

cervical vertebrae

upper jaw

lower jaw

Dimetrodon
Mammal-like reptile

Subclass: Synapsida
Order: Pelycosauria

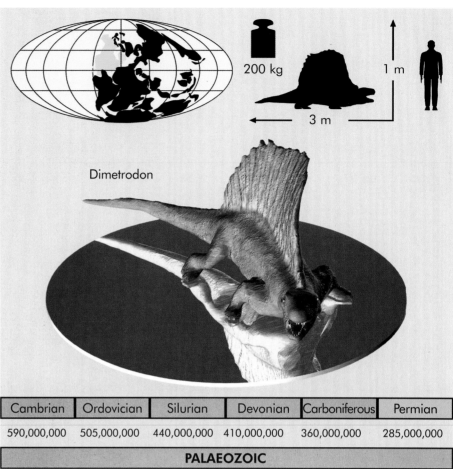

200 kg

1 m

3 m

Dimetrodon

Cambrian	Ordovician	Silurian	Devonian	Carboniferous	Permian
590,000,000	505,000,000	440,000,000	410,000,000	360,000,000	285,000,000

PALAEOZOIC

Lycaenops

Lycaenops was one of the first mammal-like reptiles. It looked very much like a dog or wolf, and was just as predatory as the latter. However, its body was not covered in hair, but scaly like that of other reptiles. Only later did the ancestors of the mammals get a hairy skin, along with external ears.

Lycaenops fossils have been found mainly in Permian Beaufort sandstones in South Africa. In fact, many finds of skulls and skeletons of fairly highly developed mammal-like reptiles (Therapsida) have been made. Lycaenops lived in the mostly dry highlands, where there were only a few rivers, where the animals could drink. Other finds have been made in the

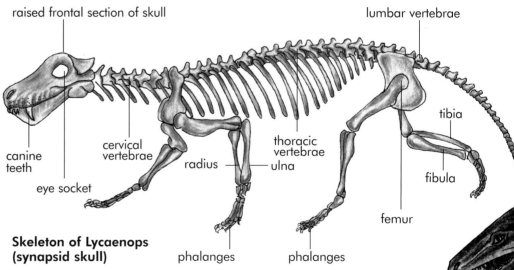

raised frontal section of skull

lumbar vertebrae

canine teeth

cervical vertebrae

eye socket

radius

ulna

thoracic vertebrae

femur

tibia

fibula

phalanges

phalanges

Skeleton of Lycaenops (synapsid skull)

western foothills of the Urals in Russia.

Lycaenops grew to up to one metre long and had a flat, 45-centimetre-long skull with long jaw muscles,

which enabled it to open its mouth wide. Particularly striking were its long canine teeth, which could tear flesh particularly well. Broad molars then crushed the food, which consisted of other animals, such as the herbivore Pareiasaurus. While Pareiasaurus was much larger, Lycaenops had no trouble killing it when it was hungry. Lycaenops usually hunted in packs.

Lyanocops' legs were positioned beneath its body as with all the mammal-like reptiles. They were slender and light, making it a good runner.

Edaphosaurus

Edaphosaurus was a medium-size Palaeozoic herbivore that lived from the late Carboniferous into the Permian period in North America and also in many parts of Europe. It belonged to the order Pelycosauria (mammal-like reptiles) in the subclass Synapsida.

Edaphosaurus was about three metres long and had a relatively small head and a lot of small teeth occupying its entire palate. This meant it had no problems chewing its food, which consisted mainly of water plants growing in the shallows at the edge of lakes and rivers. Its limbs were robust and its feet very well developed for a mammal-like reptile.

Like Dimetrodon, it too had a dorsal sail for the purpose of temperature regulation. In addition to the long spikes attached to its vertebrae, Edaphosaurus' sail also had supports running at right angles. The sail was probably brightly coloured, and alongside its temperature-regulation function, it may well have played a part in courtship displays. The animal's tail was so-to-speak a continuation of the sail.

1.6 m

3 m

Edaphosaurus

Cambrian	Ordovician	Silurian	Devonian	Carboniferous	Permian
590,000,000	505,000,000	440,000,000	410,000,000	360,000,000	285,000,000

PALAEOZOIC

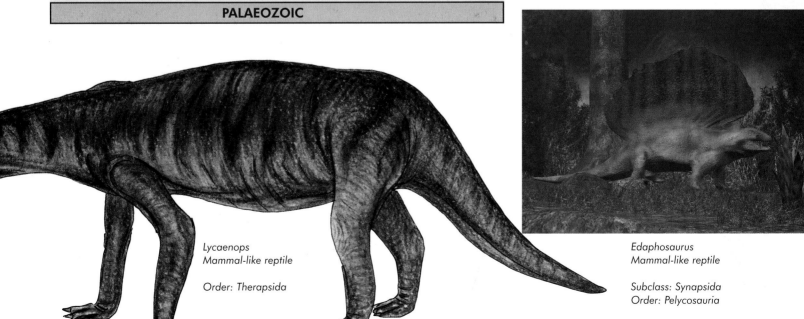

Lycaenops
Mammal-like reptile

Order: Therapsida

Edaphosaurus
Mammal-like reptile

Subclass: Synapsida
Order: Pelycosauria

CHAPTER 4

The Mesozoic Era

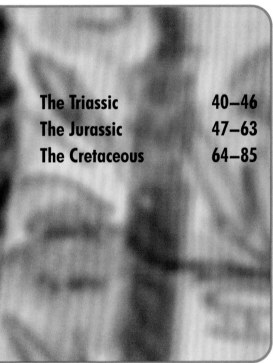

The Mesozoic Era lasted about 185 million years, and is divided into three periods, the Triassic, Jurassic and Cretaceous. It is known as the Age of the Reptiles, or of the Dinosaurs. Many marine species became extinct at the start of the Mesozoic era, including the numerous brachiopods. Armoured amphibians evolved during the Triassic into even larger forms. Tortoises and turtles, snakes and lizards were around in numerous variations. Today there are four orders of reptiles; in the Mesozoic, there are thought to have been more than 30. Insects were also on the increase. As for the world of plants, there was a great increase in ferns and conifers, and later the first broad-leaved trees, in a balanced, warm climate.

By the end of the Mesozoic era, Pangaea had totally fallen apart, and the continents drifted in various directions. Antarctica now lay at the South Pole, and had become separated from South America and Australia. India moved north, as did Africa, South America and Australia. The single ocean also split up, and the first ocean currents started. The Mesozoic era was the heyday of saurians on land, in the sea and in the air. Birds appeared, as did the first mammals. At the dawn of the Cenozoic era, the mammals were continuing to evolve and expand their territory, while the dinosaurs became totally extinct.

The Triassic

The first period of the Mesozoic, lasting from about 248 to 208 million years ago, got its name from the threefold (Greek "tri-", three) sedimentary deposits in central Europe: Bunter, Muschelkalk and Keuper.

The division of the continents was similar to that of the Permian. There was still the supercontinent Pangaea, which had a continental climate on account of the large landmass.

Ferns and horsetails, already widespread in the Permian, were now largely found in the coastal regions and wetlands. In addition, the first conifers appeared.

Many marine organisms became extinct at the end of the Permian, giving a chance for molluscs to expand. The first oysters appeared.

Of the land animals, the first mammal-like reptiles of the order Pelycosauria, including Ophiacodon, disappeared. A series of reptile

Pisanosaurus

Order: Ornithischia
Suborder: Ornithopoda
Family: Heterodontosauridae

Triassic (248–208 million years ago)

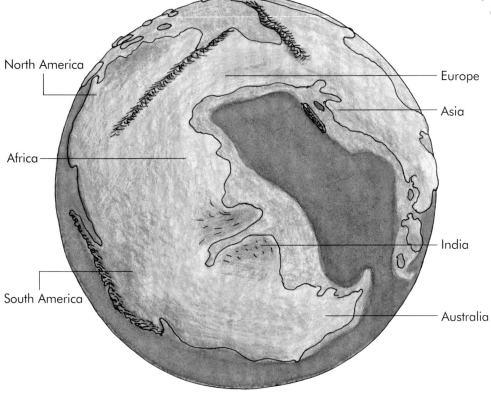

North America

Europe

Asia

Africa

India

South America

Australia

■ Ocean   ■ Land masses in the Triassic   ■ Orogeny   ■ Vegetation

groups such as lizards and fish-like saurians flourished. This period also saw the appearance of the dominant reptile groups, including the dinosaurs, pterosaurs and crocodiles. Common denizens of the shallows seas and coastal regions included the placodont ("pavement-tooth") Placodus and the marine saurian Nothosaurus.

More and more mammal-like forms appeared, including Cynognathus. The late Triassic witnessed the first true dinosaurs. These included Plateosaurus, a large herbivore, whose fossil remains were excavated in large numbers in Trossingen in Germany between 1919 and 1932.

Pisanosaurus

Pisanosaurus was the ancestor of the Ornithischia, the bird-hipped dinosaurs. These can be divided into four groups, three of which went on all fours.

The fourth group consisted of the bird-footed dinosaurs or Ornithopoda, which moved on two legs. These included Pisanosaurus, which had two relatively slender, long legs. With a body length of about 90 centimetres, this creature had a lizard-like appearance and reached speeds of about 25 kilometres an hour.

On the basis of fossil finds, we are fairly sure that Pisanosaurus belong to the family of Heterodontosauridae and lived in the Triassic, in other words several million years before other bird-hipped dinosaurs. The oldest skeleton discovered to date was found in Argentina. Large sections were preserved, including fragments of the skull and teeth, the cervical vertebrae, sections of the back and pelvis, and remains of the hand and leg bones.

The Heterodontosauridae had teeth which were strikingly different from all other dinosaurs, indeed most other reptiles. This group was the first to have clearly defined cheeks, where it could hold its food in its mouth. In the upper jaw, alongside inward-pointing molars, there were also pointed incisor-like teeth, while in the lower jaw there was only a wedge-shaped horny bar in front.

This horny bar is a typical feature of the bird-hipped dinosaurs, and is not found in any other vertebrate. The wear of the teeth that have been discovered suggests that during the chewing process, the upper and lower jaws made contact. The front teeth and horny bar presumably tore off leaves, which were then ground by the molars at the back.

The structure of the bones in the leg and foot shows that Pisanosaurus could not only execute the usual backward and forward movements, but could also move its feet to the sides. Of the five toes, the fourth and fifth were considerably shorter. The metacarpal (hand) bones of Pisanosaurus were particularly prominent, and were doubtless used for holding food.

Plateosaurus

The name "Plateosaurus" derives from the Greek words "pláte" (= plate) and "sauros" (= reptile).

Plateosaurus belonged to the Saurischia, i.e. the lizard-hipped dinosaurs. It was an early herbivorous dinosaur, which lived about 220 million years ago. It belonged to a group known as

Plataeosaurus

Infra-order: Prosauropoda
Family: Plataeosauridae

Prosauropoda, ancestors of the Sauropoda, and along with Iguanodon is one of the most famous of European dinosaurs.

Plateosaurus was a large beast, about six metres in height, and with an overall length of some ten metres. At the end of a long neck was a relatively small skull. It had numerous small teeth, and a flat lower jaw with a joint that allowed its muscles great leverage, signs that Plateosaurus was a herbivore. In the course of the further development of the Prosauropoda, the number of teeth was reduced, and they became more jagged.

In order to move its bulky body, Plateosaurus went on all fours. Only in order to pluck plants growing higher up would it stand on its hind legs. Its diet included numerous conifers and tree-ferns, like the ones discovered as fossils.

Plateosaurus' tail accounted for about half its length. The caudal vertebrae suggest that both vertical and lateral movement of the tail was possible. Powerful tail muscles helped the creature to swim.

Numerous finds of skeletons of whole Plateosaurus herds in the Keuper, a sedimentary formation in central Europe, suggest that it was gregarious. However another explanation for the mass finds is that Plateosaurus was solitary in life, but that the carcasses of the dead creatures were washed down into the river beds by the heavy downpours that occasionally interrupted the desert drought.

Lagosuchus

Many palaeontologists believe Lagosuchus to have been a direct ancestor of the dinosaurs. Only 30 centimetres long and weighing in at just 500 grams, this lightweight reptile lived in certain parts of South America during the Middle Triassic. It was very agile, probably moving as easily in the trees as on the ground. It is also thought to have been able to move around in the water.

Its nimbleness allowed it to flit rapidly over rocks and through forests and ferns, thus discouraging predators in pursuit. Lagosuchus itself ate insects, of which there was no shortage in the leafy forest. Here too, its agility was an asset.

Normally, this reptile would have run on four long, slender legs. In order to get a better view, though, it occasionally stood up on its hind legs. This way, it could recognize its enemies on time, and react accordingly.

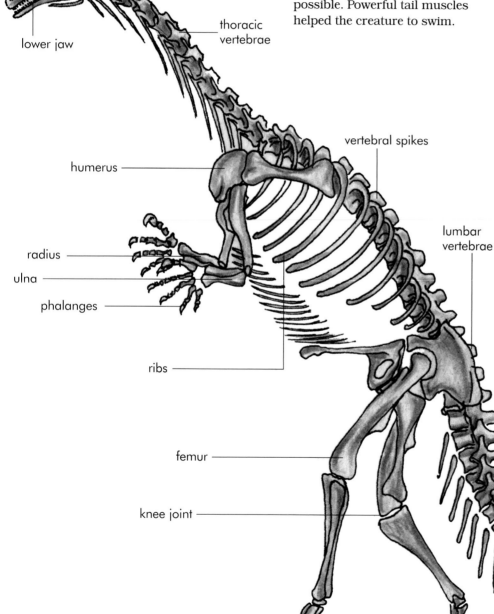

Skeleton of Plataeosaurus

upper jaw
eye socket
lower jaw
thoracic vertebrae
vertebral spikes
humerus
lumbar vertebrae
radius
ulna
phalanges
ribs
femur
knee joint
phalanges
caudal vertebrae
spiny processes

42

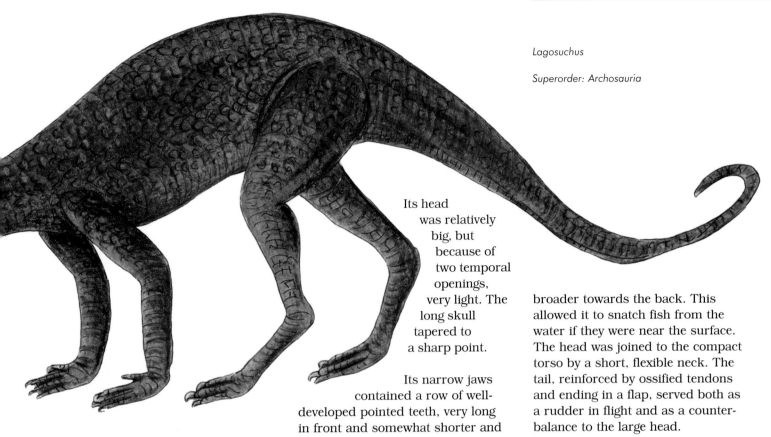

Lagosuchus

Superorder: Archosauria

Its head was relatively big, but because of two temporal openings, very light. The long skull tapered to a sharp point.

Its narrow jaws contained a row of well-developed pointed teeth, very long in front and somewhat shorter and broader towards the back. This allowed it to snatch fish from the water if they were near the surface. The head was joined to the compact torso by a short, flexible neck. The tail, reinforced by ossified tendons and ending in a flap, served both as a rudder in flight and as a counter-balance to the large head.

Evidence for its relationship to the dinosaurs is provided by the particular structure of its pelvic girdle and the position of its ankles. The shin-bones are considerably longer than the thighbones. This is a sign of a fast mover, and was also the case with the two-legged dinosaurs.

Some scientists believe that Lagosuchus was an ancestor of the pterosaurs that appeared at the end of the Triassic.

Eudimorphodon

One of the flying reptiles of the Mesozoic was Eudimorphodon. It was among the earliest representatives of the Pterosauria. This creature lived in the late Triassic. Its fossils have been found in sediments in northern Italy. Eudimorphodon belonged to the suborder Rhamphorhynchoidea, an early and primitive group of flying reptiles. It had a wingspan of about 75 centimetres and was an outstanding flier.

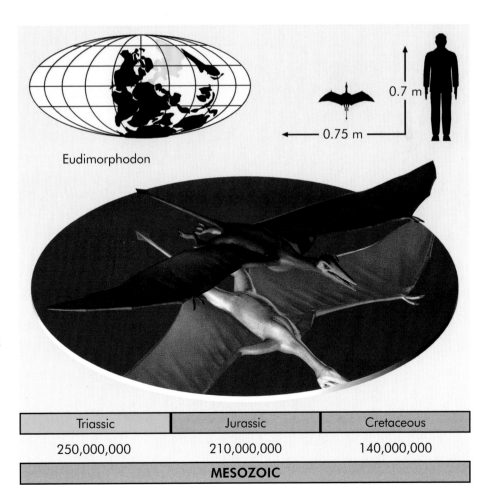

Eudimorphodon

0.7 m

0.75 m

Triassic	Jurassic	Cretaceous
250,000,000	210,000,000	140,000,000
MESOZOIC		

The wing membrane was stretched from the fourth finger across extended finger and metacarpal bones. The end of the membrane was firmly attached to the thigh. At the same time, there was a further membrane between the neck and the wrist. The breastbone was greatly flattened, providing a considerable area for the attachment of the powerful wing muscles. Eudimorphodon was widespread until the end of the Jurassic, and then became extinct.

Eudimorphodon was about 70 centimetres long. It lived in the trees. From there, it would fly out over the sea in search of food, circling at low level and catching fish swimming near the surface.

Nothosaurus

Nothosaurus belonged to one of the four groups of Mesozoic marine reptiles (Placodontia, Nothosauria, Plesiosauria, Ichthysauria). It evolved in the shallow seas of the Triassic. Some scientists think that these swimming reptiles were the ancestors of the plesiosaurs, which were among the first reptiles to adapt completely to life in the sea. Others disagree,

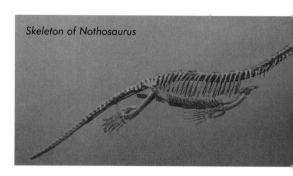

Skeleton of Nothosaurus

pointing to differences in the upper-limb girdle, and think that both groups may have had a common ancestor.

Nothosaurus presumably spent much of its life in the water, where it was constantly hunting for food,

namely fish. Its lifestyle can be compared to that of today's seals. At three metres in length, Nothosaurus had a long, slender body, as well as a long neck and tail.

Altogether, it was highly manœuvrable. Fossils indicate that it had webbed feet with five long toes. Its skull was also long and narrow. The jaws were equipped with large pointed teeth, which made it easy for it to hold on to the fish it had caught. Its legs were such that it could still walk on land.

Numerous finds, of juveniles among others, in caves and on banks indicate that Nothosaurus did spend time on land, doubtless for resting. Fossil finds are particularly concentrated in the region of the Tethys Sea and the surrounding bays and

Eudimorphodon
Flying dinosaur

Order: Pterosauria
Suborder: Ramphorhychoidea

Eudimorphodon had a body length of approx. 70 cm. It lived in the trees. From there, it went on foraging excursions to the sea for food. It would circle at low level and snatch fish swimming near the surface.

continental shelves of the time. Nothosaurus became extinct at the end of the Triassic.

Mixosaurus

The streamlined Mixosaurus was a kind of ichthyosaur. With its long beak-like snout, it bore an amazing resemblance to our dolphins, because just like them, it had to adapt to life in the open sea. These pelagic reptiles had returned from the land to the sea; their legs had become fins.

From the point of view of evolution, the family of Mixosauridae lay between the early primitive species of fish-saurians, and the later highly developed ones. Mixosaurus lived in the middle Triassic, as evidenced by

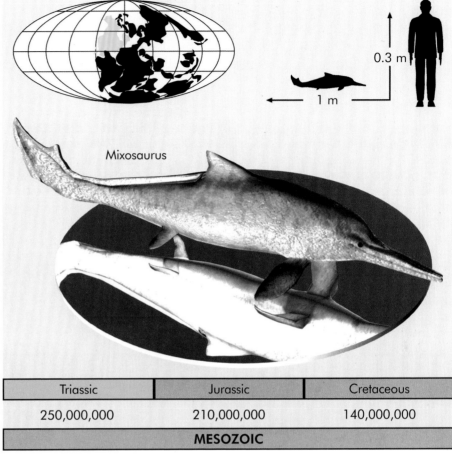

Mixosaurus

0.3 m

1 m

Triassic	Jurassic	Cretaceous
250,000,000	210,000,000	140,000,000
MESOZOIC		

Nothosaurus
Marine reptile

Order: Nothosauria
Family: Nothosauridae

numerous finds in Asia (China, Indonesia), North America (Canadian Arctic, Alaska, Nevada) and Europe. With a length of one metre, Mixosaurus had a long, narrow, fish-like body with a dorsal fin. It is presumed that it also had a small caudal fin, supported by a vertebral column that bent slightly upwards.

The limbs had become fins, somewhat like a dolphin's, with two longer ones at the front, and two shorter ones at the back. Each was composed of five toes (or fingers), much lengthened by additional bones.

Mixosaurus had a long narrow jaw, equipped with sharp teeth, in other words highly suited to catching fish. Being viviparous, Mixosaurus did not even have to return to dry land to lay eggs. In other words it was fully pelagic, totally independent of the land. Its habitat was the sea. There it could swim at 40 kilometres an hour, and go hunting the numerous fish with some ease. This viviparous species has been found chiefly in Europe and Asia.

The habitat of the Mixosaurus was the sea. There it could swim at 40 kilometres an hour, and go hunting the numerous fish with some ease. This viviparous species has been found chiefly in Europe and Asia.

Mixosaurus
Marine reptile

Order: Ichthyosauria
Family: Mixosauridae

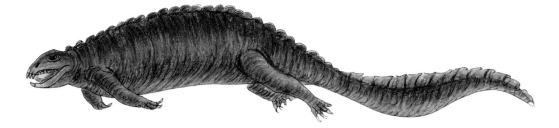

Placodus
Marine reptile

Order: Placodontia
Family: Placodontidae

Placodus

Placodus belonged to that group of marine reptiles least adapted to a life in the sea. The family of Placodontidae, also known as "pavement-toothed" saurians, preferred a life in shallow coastal waters close to the shore, where it fed predominantly on shellfish.

It had a squat body, a short neck and equally short limbs, so that it resembled the early terrestrial reptiles. The underside of its body, which lay close to the ground, was well protected by abdominal ribs. Its spinal chord was also safely housed beneath a row of bony protrusions on its back. Later species had even more armour on top and underneath.

Its skull suggests that Placodus was a specialized shellfish-eater. From its temples, powerful muscles powered its jaws, where there were rows of blunt teeth. These enabled it to harvest molluscs from the rocks. The back teeth, which were also present on the palate, were particularly broad and flat, and suited to crushing shells. The powerful jaw muscles gave it an even more powerful bite.

This reptile, which was about two metres long, appeared in the early Triassic and was around for about 35 million years. Then it died out, whereas other marine reptiles, such as Ichthyosaurus and Plesiosaurus dominated the seas for more than 100 million years. Placodus fossils have been found in Central Europe.

Cynognathus

The longest-lived group of Therapsida (mammal-like reptiles) were the Cynodontia, which means "dog-toothed". These were around for a total of 80 million years, from the late Permian to the middle Jurassic.

This suborder included Cynognathus, a mammal-like reptile, which lived in the early Triassic. It had a slender body with a head about 30 centimetres long, with an amazing resemblance to a modern dog. It had whiskers and a powerful tail. The legs were relatively long, and could be drawn up close to the body when hunting.

The creature was somewhat more than one metre long, and was among the largest of the Cynodontia.

Cynognathus probably already had a kind of hairy pelt. This made it relatively independent of the ambient temperature, for its hair allowed it to keep its body temperature constant.

The jaw had an interesting structure. Almost the entire lower jaw was formed from one single bone, which provided an anchor for the entire dentition. The teeth were already highly

Cynognathus
Mammal-like reptile

Order: Therapsida
Suborder: Cynodontia

differentiated. In the front part of the jaw there were small incisors, followed by large canine teeth, and then by sharp-edged molars. The connection with the skull was made by a continuation of the jawbone. In addition this provided a broad anchorage for the powerful jaw muscles. Cynognathus was a dangerous predator, which lived in packs in the hilly highlands of Africa, Asia and America. It was one of the most rapacious carnivores of the Triassic.

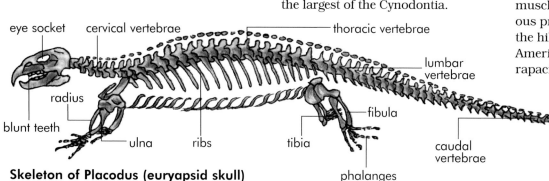

Skeleton of Placodus (euryapsid skull)

eye socket
cervical vertebrae
thoracic vertebrae
lumbar vertebrae
radius
blunt teeth
ulna
ribs
tibia
fibula
phalanges
caudal vertebrae

The Jurassic

This geological period of the Mesozoic was named after the Jura mountains of Switzerland, where there are numerous fossil deposits from this period. Particularly frequent in these deposits are ammonites and belemnites, both of them cephalopods.

Ammonites are found in great variety. Some were very small, others up to 1.8 metres long. In some, the spiral shells were smooth, in others richly decorated. Their food consisted of micro-organisms which they found near the sea-bed. Belemnites grew to up to three metres long. They were conical in form with a calcareous shell. Other marine creatures included molluscs, crabs, crinoids etc.

However reptiles and dinosaurs also took to the seas in large numbers during the Jurassic period. The best known is doubtless Ichthyosaurus, whose name means "fishlizard". It was completely adapted to life in the sea, where it had to give birth to its young.

Plesiosaurus and Elasmosaurus, both fish-eaters, were likewise among the marine creatures of the Jurassic. However, they were able to pay short visits to the shore.

The crocodiles hunted in shallow waters, but could also swim kilometres out to sea. On land, reptiles became very widespread. This is particularly true of the sauromorphs, which includes dinosaurs, pterosaurs, lizards, snakes and crocodiles.

The other main branch comprised the mammal-like reptiles or theromorphs, which had its heyday in the Permian and Triassic. By the Jurassic, they had been replaced by their successors, the mammals.

Jurassic fern

During the Jurassic, the huge land masses broke up into smaller continents. The advance of shallow seas brought rain to regions that had previously been deserts. In some areas, the climate was hot and humid, with luxuriant vegetation. In this environment, the dinosaurs were able to develop splendidly, with the appearance of many new species.

Towards the end of the Jurassic, 145 million years ago, the northern and southern continents split apart. North America broke away from Africa, but remained attached to northern Europe. India doubtless moved northwards from then on. Between Africa and the still contiguous land masses of Europe and

North America, and between North America and Asia, shallow seas spread over the low-lying land. There were no polar ice-caps, which would otherwise have bound up a lot of the water. The warm climate continued into the Cretaceous. Under the influence of heavy rainfalls, huge ferns, conifers and ginkgoes developed. They grew above all around the estuaries of the rivers, which often flooded, laying down fertile alluvial deposits.

In these marshy forests, huge herbivores like Brachiosaurus and Apatosaurus could enjoy ideal living conditions. Stegosauria such as

Fossil dragonfly

Stegosaurus in North America and Tuojiangosaurus in Asia attained their greatest species diversity towards the end of the Jurassic. Some groups even survived until the end of the Cretaceous.

Alongside the herbivores, numerous large and small predatory dinosaurs also spread out over all the continents. Among the largest were Dilophosaurus and Allosaurus. The smaller, nimble species included Compsognathus, which was no bigger than a chicken. It lived primarily on insects such as dragonflies, and other small creatures.

The first known bird, Archaeopteryx, dates from about the same time.

Archaeopteryx lithographica

Suborder: Theropoda
Family: Archaeopterygidae

Archaeopteryx lithographica

The first Archaeopteryx skeleton was found in 1861 in a 150-million-year-old layer of limestone in Solnhofen, southern Germany. It was almost completely preserved. Next to the fine bones, impressions of feathers on tails and wings were discovered. An even better-preserved skeleton was unearthed in the direct vicinity in about 1875. Around eleven such fossils have since been found, all of them from layers of limestone.

Anatomically, Archaeopteryx (Greek for "ancient wing", or bird) might represent a link between reptiles and birds, but it is probably a side-line of the bird family rather than a direct ancestor.

Because of its opposable toes and the formation of its wrist, the Archaeopteryx was classified as a bird. Other typical bird features were the feathers on its wings (arms) and tail, and the furcula, or wishbone, which formed from the two fused collarbones. In other respects, the Archaeopteryx could quite easily be taken for a small, bipedal carnivore.

The Archaeopteryx was about the size of a pigeon. It had a small head with large eyes and sharp teeth in its upper and lower jaw. Its tail was long and bony. The skeleton of the 35-centimetre-long creature had many reptilian characteristics including the long tail, abdominal ribs, brain structure and tooth-lined jaws.

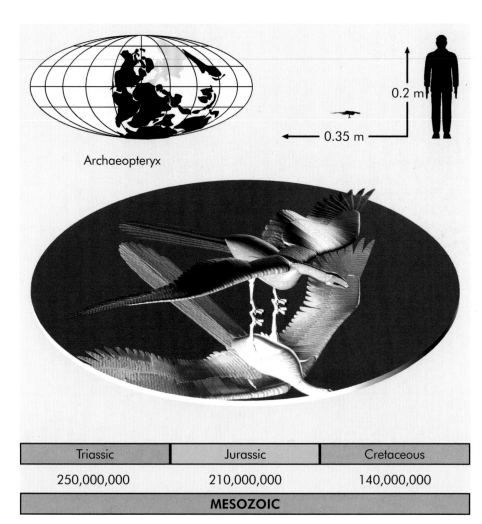

Archaeopteryx

0.2 m

0.35 m

Triassic	Jurassic	Cretaceous
250,000,000	210,000,000	140,000,000
MESOZOIC		

The Archaeopteryx probably inhabited forests where it fed mainly on insects. It is likely that the Archaeopteryx fluttered from tree to tree, rather than flew. Its wingspan measured around 45 centimetres. The function of its feathers is unclear. Either they helped the Archaeopteryx fly or they kept it warm when it was perched high up in the treetops.

Teratosaurus

Among the oldest known meat-eating giant lizards were the members of the Megalosauridae family to which the Teratosaurus belonged. Teeth from a Teratosaurus were found in Germany. With such little information to go by, it was difficult for palaeontologists to classify the Teratosaurus.

After the first fossils were found and ascribed to the late Triassic, fragments of a skeleton from a similar specimen were discovered in South Africa. These dated back to the early Jurassic period. Using just a few bone fragments, a reconstruction of the Teratosaurus was created and the following conclusions were drawn: the Teratosaurus was a stout, meat-eating reptile with a large head, a short, muscular neck and a long, rigid tail. It had powerful arms with three-clawed fingers, and it ran on two strong, long hind legs with three-toed feet.

With its strong claws, the Teratosaurus was capable of ripping up even large animals. Its numerous sharp teeth helped it tear up its prey. The Teratosaurus was approximately six metres long and weighed between 200 and 350 kilograms.

Teratosaurus

Order: Saurischia
Suborder: Theropoda
Family: Megalosauridae

a lizard-like appearance and ran swiftly in an upright position on two slender legs. Its arms were short, its body supple and its sinuous neck ended in a relatively short head.

Only skull fragments and the jaw bones of an Echinodon have been found. These revealed what unusual teeth the animal had. These had a very uniform appearance and looked more like those of a lizard such as the Heterondonto-saurus.

Echinodon

The Echinodon, a member of the Ornithischia order, belonged to the bird-footed Heterodontosauridae family of fast-moving, bipedal dinosaurs.

The Echinodon was a small animal only 60 centimetres long. It had

The only Echinodon finds were made in England. Heterodontosauridae family, to which Echinodon belongs, is thought to have lived all over the world.

Echinodon

Order: Ornithischia
Suborder: Ornithopoda
Family: Heterodontosauridae

49

Diplodocus skeleton

Diplodocus

The Diplodocus (Greek: dokós = beam) belonged to the big plant-eating group of Saurischia (lizard-hipped dinosaurs). It originated in the upper Malm (an epoch during the Jurassic period) and was found mainly in North America.

With a body length of 25 to 30 metres, it weighed "only" ten tons. This was because of its lightweight vertebrae. The almost hollow bones were held together by their strong exterior and bundles of muscles. As a comparison, the Brachiosaurus weighed up to 80 tons.

The slender trunk of the Diplodocus was only around four metres long, its thin neck, however, over seven metres. This ended in a small, elongated skull, measuring about 60 centimetres. Weak, peg-like teeth formed a filter-like construction enabling it to ingest food. Its diet consisted of water plants, molluscs and small animals. Diplodocus lived in large herds in the swamps and forests of North America. Apart from water plants, it also ate fresh young branches from the tops of conifer trees.

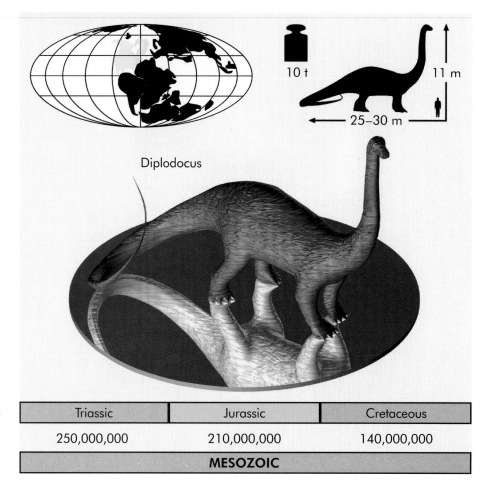

10 t

11 m

25–30 m

Diplodocus

Triassic	Jurassic	Cretaceous
250,000,000	210,000,000	140,000,000
MESOZOIC		

Diplodocus

Order: Saurischia
Infraorder: Sauropoda
Family: Diplodocidae

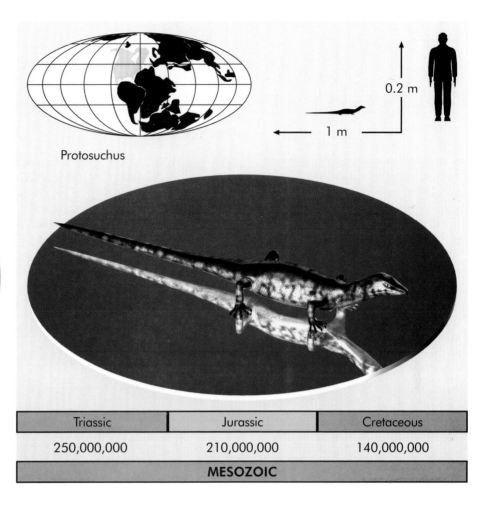

Protosuchus

0.2 m

1 m

Triassic	Jurassic	Cretaceous
250,000,000	210,000,000	140,000,000
MESOZOIC		

Protosuchus

Protosuchus belonged to the most successful group of Archosauria (superorder of reptiles). It was a terrestrial crocodile, something we know because fossil remains of the Protosuchus were found together with dinosaur fossils. These discoveries were made in Arizona, North America, in layers of the early Jurassic period.

The one-metre-long crocodile had a flat, longish skull. Its short jaws became wider at the back. The muscles were located at the back of the mouth, enabling the animal to open its mouth wide to swallow its prey.

A dividing bony plate between the roof of the mouth and nasal cavity made it possible for the crocodile to breathe and eat simultaneously.

At the front of the jaws, the Protosuchus had two strong canine teeth which fitted exactly into notches in its upper jaw when it closed its mouth.

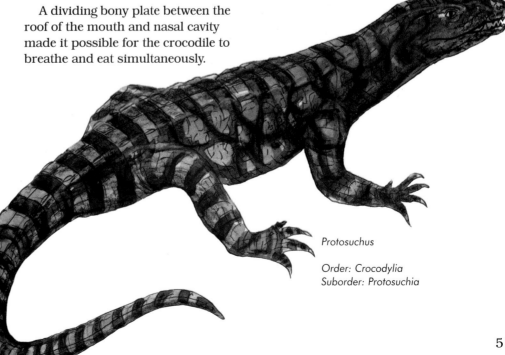

Protosuchus

Order: Crocodylia
Suborder: Protosuchia

51

Dilophosaurus

This large, two-legged carnivore belonging to the order of lizard-hipped dinosaurs (Saurischia) lived 200 million years ago in the early Jurassic period. Its name means "lizard with two combs". Its most striking feature: two parallel bony crests on its head which gave the animal its name.

It is still not clear why these crests existed. They were too thin and fragile to be of use in self-defence. They either helped the Dilophosaurus regulate its body temperature or they were used to impress females during courtship rituals or to settle amorous conflicts with rivals.

The Dilophosaurus had a lightweight, slender body, a long tail and long, slim legs. It grew to a total length of six metres, in other words twice as long as its predecessors from the Triassic. It weighed approximately 500 kilograms.

The pelvic structure of the Dilophosaurus was not well formed and consisted only of four sacral vertebrae. This may be an indication that the Dilophosaurus spent much of its time in water where the weight of its body was buoyed up. The carnivore probably did not live only in the water but was also able to move swiftly and nimbly on two legs. On land, it used its claw-like hands and feet to hunt for its favourite food – plant-eating dinosaurs as well as rotting carcasses.

Rhamphorhynchus

Rhamphorhynchus was a flying reptile (Pterosauria) that lived in the late Jurassic period. Rhamphorhynchus skeletons were found in England and Tanzania, as well as in in layers of limestone in Solnhofen (southern Germany) where remains of the Archaeopteryx were also discovered. These remains revealed the structure of the wing membrane particularly clearly. It was leathery and filled with thin fibres. Similar to bats, the membrane stretched over the elongated finger bones.

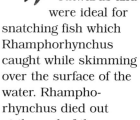

The rear end of the wing was connected to the thigh. The wingspan of the one-metre-long Rhamphorhynchus measured 75 centimetres. The slender body ended in a long tail with a flap of skin at its tip which was reinforced by ossified tendons. This probably helped the Rhamphorhynchus steer.

Compared with the body, its head was relatively large although slight in build. Its neck was rather short. The narrow jaws of Rhamphorhynchus were lined with large, sharp teeth.

Their tips bent outwards and were ideal for snatching fish which Rhamphorhynchus caught while skimming over the surface of the water. Rhamphorhynchus died out at the end of the Jurassic period.

Rhamphorhynchus

Order: Pterosauria
Suborder: Rhamphorhynchoidea

Dilophosaurus

Order: Saurischia
Suborder: Theropoda

Stegosaurus

This plant-eating dinosaur from the order of bird-hipped dinosaurs or Ornithischia, lived 150 million years ago. It was an armoured dinosaur and is today one of the most famous because of its imposing appearance. Stegosaurus was the biggest representative of the Stegosauridae family. It was between six and nine metres long and weighed up to two tons.

The Stegosaurus had a series of bony plates on its back. These were not connected to the skeleton but were embedded in its skin, which is why their arrangement is not quite clear. They probably stood upright in two rows, and were staggered.

Palaeontologists are still not sure today whether these 60-centimetre-long bony plates were used in visual communication or whether they protected the vertebrae of the Stegosaurus against large carnivores. Or were they heat regulators, extending the body's surface to

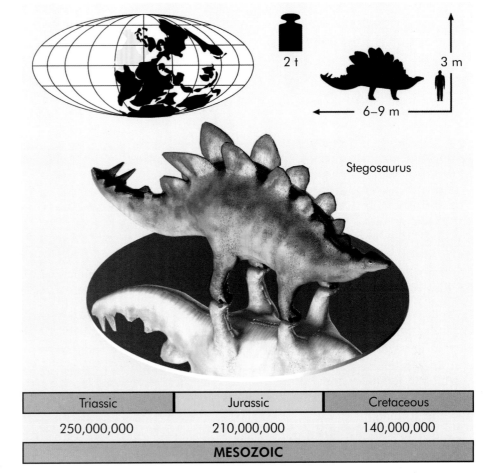

Stegosaurus

Triassic	Jurassic	Cretaceous
250,000,000	210,000,000	140,000,000
MESOZOIC		

absorb the heat of the sun?

The tail of the Stegosaurus featured sharp, horny spikes which were most certainly used in self-defence. The Stegosaurus was able to wave its tail to and fro.

Long spiny processes on the dorsal and caudal vertebrae provided support for very strong back muscles. The Stegosaurus was therefore able to rear up onto its hind legs and forage for

food amongst the treetops. Its staple diet, however, probably consisted of small plants which were available in abundance in the jungle.

The skull of the Stegosaurus was comparatively small, as was its brain. The jaw was beak-like and contained small teeth at the back. This made chewing difficult which is why the Stegosaurus, like other plant-eaters, swallowed stones (gastroliths) which helped grind food. Once the stones had worn down, they were replaced by new ones.

A particularly striking feature of the Stegosaurus was its strong hind legs, which were twice as long as its front legs. Because it normally moved on all fours, its body sloped forward steeply from the region of the pelvis.

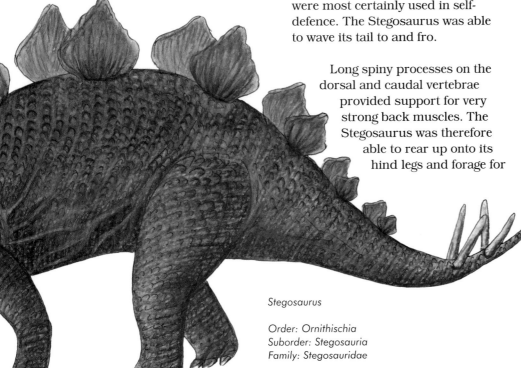

Stegosaurus

Order: Ornithischia
Suborder: Stegosauria
Family: Stegosauridae

53

Allosaurus

Allosaurus

Order: Saurischia
Suborder: Theropoda
Family: Allosauridae

The biggest predator which lived in the late Jurassic period 156 to 130 million years ago was the Allosaurus. Allosaurus means "different lizard" (allos = other, sauros = reptile). It was not until millions of years later that the Allosaurus was outmatched in size by the Tyrannosaurus. Allosaurus is a lizard-hipped dinosaur (Saurischia) of the infraorder Carnosauria (large meat-eating dinosaurs). Remains have been found mainly in the Morrison Formation of North America and Portugal.

This large, cumbersome monster reached a length of over 12 metres (the size of a bus) and was 4.6 metres tall. It could weigh anything up to two tons. It had a bulky body and sturdy feet with sharp, three-fingered claws. It used these to kill its prey, which it then tore into pieces with its claw-like hands and powerful sabre-like teeth.

Its diet consisted of plant-eaters such as the Apatosaurus and Stegosaurus. Its prey was often as big as the Allosaurus itself, which meant that it sustained the creature for a long time. Allosaurus probably stalked its prey, like lions today. Some palaeontologists believe Allosaurus was a scavenger and survived on rotting carcasses. Whatever the case, it ate the meat of plant-eating animals. Impressions of its teeth on the skeletons of such animals provide proof of this.

The skull of the Allosaurus was large but contained large openings which reduced its weight. Individual skull bones (with the exception of the jaw bone) usually grow together. In the case of the Allosaurus, however, the loose bones provided support for strong chewing muscles. It was able to open its mouth extremely wide and swallow huge chunks of meat. The jawbone and top of the skull were the only solid bones, providing protection for the brain. They also supported muscles needed for chewing.

The eyes of Allosaurus were almost twice the size of those of the far larger meat-eating Tyrannosaurus. Strong brow horns above the eyes offered Allosaurus protection when fighting for prey. They might also have protected against sunlight. Allosaurus probably defended its territory by head-butting.

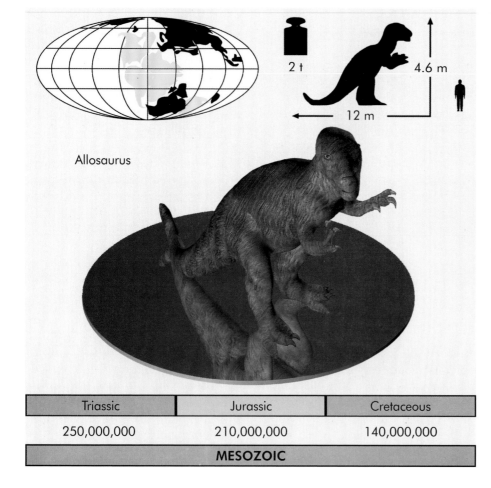

2 t   4.6 m

12 m

Allosaurus

Triassic	Jurassic	Cretaceous
250,000,000	210,000,000	140,000,000
MESOZOIC		

Its stout, muscular neck enabled the Allosaurus to move its head energetically. With powerful swiping movements, it was able to defend its prey. It also helped it balance when running. The spinal column consisted of vertebrae with long processes which provided support for powerful muscles.

Allosaurus had around 40 teeth in its upper jaw and slightly fewer in its lower jaw. They were up to ten centimetres long and serrated on two sides like a knife for cutting meat. They pointed backwards to prevent prey from escaping the Allosaurus' mouth. If the teeth were worn or broken, news ones grew in their place.

The Allosaurus lived and hunted in pairs or herds in the lower highlands in the western part of North America (basis of today's Rocky Mountains). Rivers ran down these mountains, and on their banks dense tropical forests flourished.

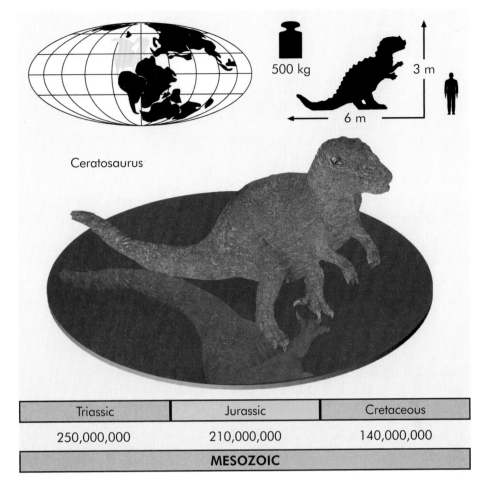

Ceratosaurus

500 kg   3 m   6 m

Triassic	Jurassic	Cretaceous
250,000,000	210,000,000	140,000,000
MESOZOIC		

Ceratosaurus

Order: Saurischia
Suborder: Theropoda
Family: Ceratosauridae

Ceratosaurus

Ceratosaurus was a slightly built carnivore from the Jurassic period. It belonged to the Saurischia order and suborder of Theropoda (meat-eaters). Fossils were found by Marsh and Cope in Colorado and Wyoming, but also in East Africa.

The Ceratosaurus was approximately six metres long. It stood on two legs and had a forward-leaning body, which was held in balance by a long, rigid tail. Its front legs were shorter than its hind legs. Like birds, it held its head at a right angle to its neck. Its compact skull, which was relatively light because of several temporal openings, had a strong jawbone consisting of loose bones, making the mouth flexible.

The Ceratosaurus was able to open its mouth very wide and swallow large pieces of meat without any problem. Facial muscles connected the openings of the skull and thus formed bridges between the bones.

On its nasal bones, ridge-shaped projections were located behind the nostrils. These were covered with horn when the Ceratosaurus was alive. Ceratosaurus sported a short horn on its nose, the purpose of which is unknown. It might have been important during fights with rivals or it was used to impress females.

Some researchers believe the horn helped juvenile dinosaurs hatch from their eggs. All these bulges and protrusions gave the Ceratosaurus a rather bizarre appearance.

Long, sharp teeth, which bent inwards and grew back again, were suitable for tearing up large prey. This consisted of Sauropods (long-necked plant-eaters) which inhabited swampland and surrounding areas. In the warm, humid climate, plants such as ferns and horsetail grew in profusion. The Ceratosaurus was probably a solitary animal.

Skull of a brachiosaurid

Brachiosaurus

One of the largest four-legged herbivores was the Brachiosaurus. It belonged to the Saurischia order (lizard-hipped dinosaurs) of the suborder Sauropodomorpha (long-necked, plant-eating dinosaurs) and the Brachiosauridae family, believed together with the Titanosaurs, to be the biggest of the long-necked plant-eaters. It lived 157 to 145 million years ago in the Jurassic period. The first Brachiosaurus specimen was found in 1900 in Colorado, USA, and it was given its scientific name in 1903. From 1908 to 1912, sensational finds were made in Tanzania (East Africa) where the German scientists Henning and Janensch were taking part in an expedition. During the late Jurassic period, this was a huge wooded flood plain and river delta with numerous sand banks. In the 1980s these finds were allocated their own sister group, Giraffatitan. Today, this fully assembled Giraffatitan skeleton can be admired at the Palaeontological Museum in Berlin.

The Brachiosaurus grew to an enormous 12.5 metres. It was 23 metres long and weighed up to 40 tons. Its average shoulder height was around six metres. Its humerus bone alone measured two metres. Because of its weight, the Brachiosaurus was probably unable to stand on its hind legs. But with a head height of 12.5 metres, this was not necessary. The Brachiosaurus could pick the leaves off treetops like a giraffe. It also ate ferns and conifers.

It had no molars so had to swallow plant parts whole. It occasionally swallowed gizzard stones or gastroliths, which helped the stomach muscles grind food.

Physically, the Brachiosaurus looked very much like other sauropods. It had a small head with a concavity and a flat snout containing large, spatulate teeth. Its large nostrils were located on top of the skull. This initially led researchers to believe the Brachiosaurus lived predominantly in water. Here it kept its nostrils above the water surface in order to breathe.

Over half of the Brachiosaurus' body length consisted of neck. It did not have more cervical vertebrae than other dinosaurs, but they were three times longer than the dorsal vertebrae. For the Brachiosaurus to be able to support its bulky body, there were large cavities at the side of the vertebrae which ended in numerous

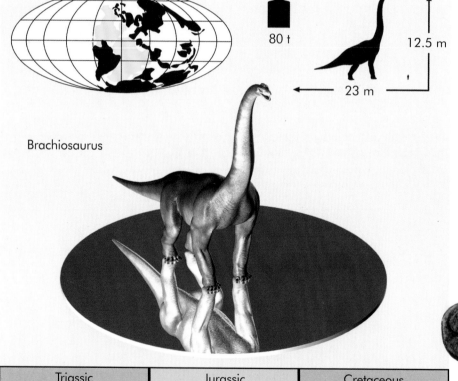

Brachiosaurus

80 t

12.5 m

23 m

Triassic	Jurassic	Cretaceous
250,000,000	210,000,000	140,000,000
MESOZOIC		

Brachiosaurus

Order: Saurischia
Infraorder: Sauropoda
Family: Brachiosauridae

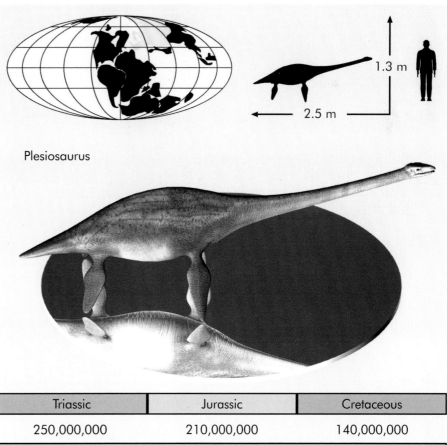

Skeleton reconstruction of a Giraffatitan brancai at the Naturkundemuseum in Berlin

shoulders, it formed a steeply sloping line, similar to a giraffe's back today.

Plesiosaurus

Plesiosauria (flippered lizards) were among the most successful marine reptiles of the Mesozoic Era. One of the earliest members of the group was the Plesiosaurus in the early Jurassic period.

The earliest Plesiosaurus already combined all the main features. Its body, which could grow to a length of 2.5 metres, was compact, its neck

bony struts. This made the skeleton slightly lighter but the struts also supported the body. The pelvic girdle was also firmly connected to the sacral vertebrae and supported the body.

The legs of Brachiosaurus were thick and column-like. The front

legs were longer than the hind legs, a peculiarity of the Brachiosauridae. Each of the limbs had five splayed toes or fingers. The long, thick tail ended in a sharp point. From the

1.3 m

2.5 m

Plesiosaurus

Triassic	Jurassic	Cretaceous
250,000,000	210,000,000	140,000,000
MESOZOIC		

Plesiosaurus   Order: Plesiosauria
                Family: Plesiosauridae

Marine reptile

Hunting for fish in the water, the Plesiosaurus was as fast as an arrow. Coming ashore to lay its eggs, it moved only very slowly.

quite long in relation to its body, the tail short. Its limbs developed into long, paddle-shaped flappers but moved up and down like the wings of a bird rather than paddles. Their ends were rounded like wings. Their toes and fingers consisted of up to ten bones (usually five or fewer). Shoulder blade and hips were fairly flat to provide plenty of support for limb muscles.

The belly ribs connected the bones of the pectoral girdle and pelvis and protected the body's soft parts from the bottom of the belly. This was important because the females had to go ashore to lay their eggs. They moved forward laboriously using their paddles. The eggs were probably laid in a sandpit.

The Plesiosaurus hunted for fish. It was not particularly fast but its long neck made it an agile animal.

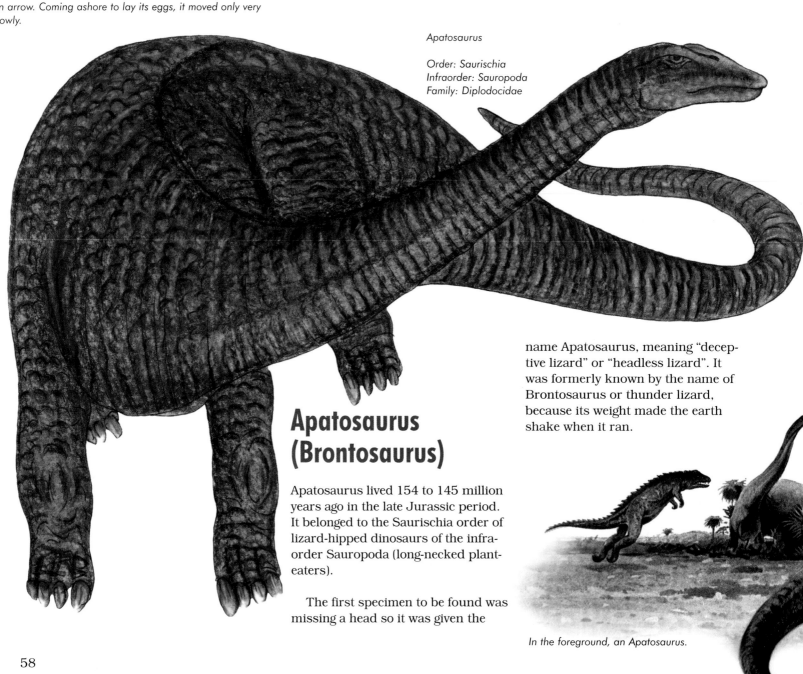

Apatosaurus

Order: Saurischia
Infraorder: Sauropoda
Family: Diplodocidae

Apatosaurus (Brontosaurus)

Apatosaurus lived 154 to 145 million years ago in the late Jurassic period. It belonged to the Saurischia order of lizard-hipped dinosaurs of the infra-order Sauropoda (long-necked plant-eaters).

The first specimen to be found was missing a head so it was given the

name Apatosaurus, meaning "deceptive lizard" or "headless lizard". It was formerly known by the name of Brontosaurus or thunder lizard, because its weight made the earth shake when it ran.

In the foreground, an Apatosaurus.

Apatosaurus was a bulky plant-eater with a plump body, long neck, small head and long tail. With a shoulder height of 4.5 metres, it grew to over 21.3 metres in length. It weighed around 30 tons and was probably unable to run any faster than eight kilometres an hour. Even a thighbone in its four column-like legs was 1.5 metres long. Each foot had five clawed toes on the front legs and three on the hind legs.

The brain of the Apatosaurus was tiny. It was even smaller than part of the ventral nerve chord in the hip region, which might have transmitted messages from the tail, almost like a second brain. The tail simultaneously helped the animal maintain its balance when it reared up to graze from tall treetops. The Apatosaurus also used its tail to defend itself against rivals, swinging it about like a whip.

The structure of the Apatosaurus' 82 vertebrae was very different. The cervical vertebrae were lightweight because they contained hollow areas. The very compact thoracic vertebrae had long processes to support strong

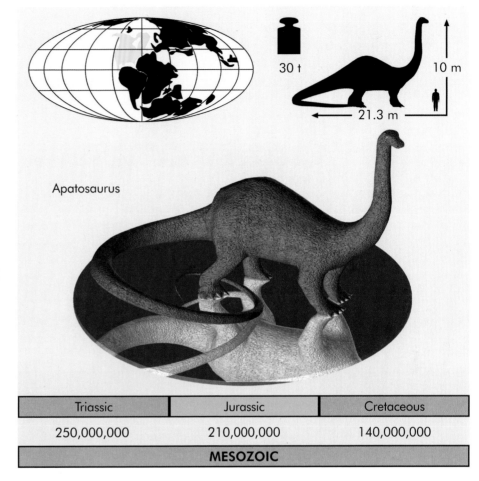

30 t   10 m

21.3 m

Apatosaurus

Triassic	Jurassic	Cretaceous
250,000,000	210,000,000	140,000,000

MESOZOIC

muscles. The caudal vertebrae were light and more slender in build to provide plenty of support for muscles.

Apatosaurus had large, lightweight, blunt teeth that were typical of plant-eaters. New ones grew in the place of old, worn out ones. Such weak teeth were not capable of

grinding most hard-fibred plants (ferns and leaves of trees), which is why the Apatosaurus swallowed stones to help break up food in the stomach, like geese today. This explains why stones are frequently found next to the footprints of plant-eaters, because the stones were gradually regurgitated. Some researchers believe that undigested seeds were also excreted. These then germinated and prevented the land from becoming overgrazed.

Apatosaurus lived on dry land. Tracks show that it lived in herds, like many animals today. Juveniles remained in the middle of the herds for protection against predators while the older, stronger animals roamed on the periphery.

Megalosaurus

Megalosaurus was a member of the Saurischia order (lizard-hipped dinosaur) which belonged to the group of bipedal carnivores. It lived 170 to 155 million years ago in the Jurassic period.

The first dinosaur finds were made in England in 1822. In a slate quarry in Stonesfield, Oxfordshire (southern England), the carnivorous Megalosaurus was found next to the plant-eating Iguanodon. Megalosaurus means "giant lizard".

Megalosaurus was nine metres long and three metres tall. It weighed roughly 900 kilograms. Its head was heavily built with a powerful jawbone. Its muscular neck joined a stout body with strong hind legs and a short, powerful tail. The slightly shorter front limbs ended in five-fingered hands with claws, enabling it to grab its prey.

It hunted mainly peaceable plant-eaters (sauropods) and Ornithischia (bird-hipped dinosaurs). With its long, sharp teeth, which were bent at the ends and flat at the

sides, it had no problem chewing up its prey.

Apart from finds in southern England, fossilized remains of the Megalosaurus were also discovered in France and Portugal.

Heterodontosaurus

Heterodontosaurus was a member of the bird-hipped order of dinosaurs (Ornithischia) from the Jurassic period. It belonged to the suborder of Ornithopoda (bird-footed dinosaur) and was a plant-eater like all Ornithischia.

At first glance, the Heterodontosaurus bore a strong resemblance to the oldest members of the Ornithopod family, the small Heterodontosauridae, to which the Echinodon also belongs. Different types of teeth were characteristic of this

Megalosaurus

Order: Saurischia
Suborder: Therapoda
Family: Megalosauridae

dinosaur, such that its bite was similar to that of mammals. However, there is no evolutionary connection.

Heterodontosaurus ("lizard with different types of teeth") was a light-footed bipedal animal which was around 85 centimetres long. When in a hurry, it probably moved on two legs. When searching for food (digging up roots), its relatively long forelegs suggest it probably used all four. The extremities of the Heterodontosaurus each had

four toes with sharp claws which curled around the hands. These are the more primitive features of the bird-footed dinosaur.

A more advanced development, on the other hand, is the formation of its teeth. Like the meat-eaters, the Heterodontosaurus had several types of teeth: sharp teeth in the front top jaw, similar to incisors, only a horny beak in the lower jaw, and at the back, at the top and bottom, were large canine teeth which were sharp and bent. Next to these was a row of molars with ridges which helped grind up plants. The Heterodontosaurus used its front teeth to tear off leaves. The function of the canine teeth is not yet clear. Such teeth are usually used by carni-

Mamenchisaurus

Order: Saurischia
Suborder: Sauropoda
Family: Mamenchi-
sauridae

cessfully, the Heterodontosauria disappeared without a trace for reasons that are still unknown. The line of Ornithopoda consequently came to an abrupt end.

Remains of the Heterodontosaurus were discovered for the first time in 1962 in South Africa. Initially only the skull of the animal was found, which is roughly the size of a rabbit skull. Later the complete skeleton was discovered.

Mamenchisaurus

The Mamenchisaurus belonged to the large, long-necked herbivores (Sauropoda) of the order Saurischia (lizard-hipped dinosaurs). It lived 155 to 145 million years ago in the late Jurassic period in China.

Its relatively slender body measured a total length of 22 metres, 11 metres of which was its neck. This consisted of 19 cervical vertebrae, each of which was twice as long as the dorsal vertebrae. The vertebrae had long struts running between them to give the skeleton additional support.

The head of the Mamenchisaurus was very small, its neck not very supple. It moved a little like the jib of a crane. Unlike other sauropods, the tail, which measured only five to six metres, did not counterbalance the length of the neck.

Its extra-long neck gave the Mamenchisaurus an advantage over other plant-eaters: if it reared up on its strong hind legs, it was able to reach even the highest branches of a tree.

vores to tear up pieces of meat.
Skulls have been found with and without canine teeth so it is possible that only the males had canines which they used when fighting. The way in which the teeth were worn down shows that the Heterodontosaurus could not only chew up and down but also sideways. Despite developing suc-

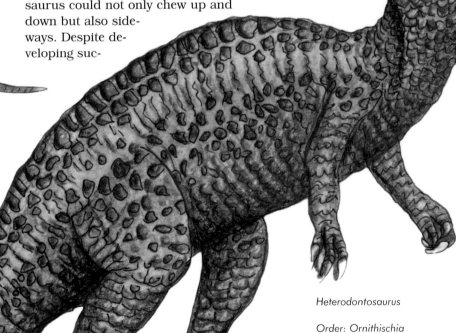

Heterodontosaurus

Order: Ornithischia
Suborder: Ornithopoda
Family: Heterodontosauridae

61

Camarasaurus

This species of sauropod (long-necked plant-eater) belonged to the group of Saurischia (lizard-hipped dinosaurs). Camarasaurus lived 155 to 145 million years ago in the late Jurassic period.

It grew to a length of up to 18 metres and weighed some 18 tons. Its compact skull and slightly elevated snout contained four dozen spoon-shaped teeth which were very robust, enabling the Camasaurus to chew even tough, hard parts of plants. It found these in abundance on the banks of lakes and on humid, tropical plains where the Camasaurus probably lived in herds. To help its digestion, the Camarasaurus swallowed gizzard stones. When they had worn down, they were regurgitated and replaced by new ones.

The Camarasaurus had large eyes and an especially large nasal opening, the function of which is still not known. It might have cooled the brain. The old and young animals lived together in herds. In times of drought, they sometimes roamed great distances in

search of fertile regions. Skeletons of young animals found in 1922 in Utah revealed that its head was relatively big (five metres long) and its neck short. Proportions changed as the animal grew older: it developed a long, muscular neck which ended in a small head. The Camarasaurus lived primarily in North America.

Kentrosaurus

Kentrosaurus, meaning "sharp lizard", was the African relative of the North American Stegosaurus but was smaller and had more densely arranged plates and spikes. It belonged to the suborder Stegosauria (spiked dinosaurs) of the order Ornithischia (bird-hipped dinosaurs). It was indigenous to Africa where it lived around 150 million years ago in the late Jurassic period.

After a German engineer discovered the fossilized bones of a giant dinosaur near the village of Tendaguru in 1907, the director of the Berlin Museum of Natural

Camarasaurus

Order: Saurischia
Infraorder: Sauropoda
Family: Camarasauridae

Kentrosaurus

Order: Ornithischia
Suborder: Stegosauria
Family: Stegosauridae

Sciences organized an expedition to carry out excavation work. It was one of the most extensive excavations of all times. The village of Tendaguru could only be reached after a four-day march through the jungle, some 70 kilometres from the coast.

Between 1909 and 1911, over 4,000 consignments of bones were dispatched to distant harbours. Finds included a well-preserved, 23-metre long Brachiosaurus skeleton and the skeleton of a Kentrosaurus. It was 4.5 metres long and sported triangular plates, which probably stood upright, on neck and shoulders. Sharp spikes protruded from its back and tail.

Although its hind legs were more strongly developed and longer than the front legs, the Kentrosaurus walked on all fours. It appears that it was only able to move forwards in a hunch-backed position with a lurching gait. With its long, almost tooth-less jaw, Like all Stegosaurs, it fed exclusively on plants.

Tuojiangosaurus

The Tuojiangosaurus lived in China 157 to 154 million years ago in the late Jurassic period. It belonged to the family Stegosauridae of the Ornithischia order (bird-hipped dinosaurs). It was the first of the Stegosauridae to be found in Asia. An almost complete skeleton was discovered here.

Reaching a length of up to seven metres, its build was similar to that of the Stegosaurus, whose most distinctive feature was the bony plates that ran along its back. The Tuojiangosaurus had a compact trunk. The small, sharp bony plates on its back became longer and more thorn-like in the region of the hip. The tip of its tail was equipped with a pair of long thorns which were a dangerous weapon.

With its small, flat head and spoon-shaped teeth, the Tuojiangosaurus probably found food among low-growing plants such as ferns. Unlike the Stegosaurus, it was unable to stand on its hind legs because it lacked important spiny processes to provide support for muscles.

Tuojiangosaurus

Order: Ornithischia
Suborder: Stegosauria
Family: Stegosauridae

The Cretaceous

The section of the geological era after the Jurassic period was named after the white limestone deposits that were typical of this system. The term "Chalk Age" was first used by a German geologist by the name of Karl von Raumner in 1815, and translated into English as "Cretaceous". Chalk cliffs from this period can still be found today in Dover, on the coast of England.

This last phase of the Mesozoic era lasted from 144 to 65 million years ago. This was the heyday of dinosaurs, before the animals disappeared altogether, a mystery that remains unresolved to this day. During this period, the already divided supercontinent of Pangaea split up into smaller parts. Northern and southern sections drifted further apart, the Atlantic Ocean increased in size.

Floods occurred in large parts of the continent and shallow seas formed. North America was particularly affected. Flooding initially began in the South. A huge gulf evolved,

Chalky sandstone with belemnites

covering what is now Texas and Mexico.

Bodies of water also expanded in the North so that eventually only a bridge of land connected the two big regions not covered by water. This bridge finally disappeared too, allowing the two oceans to merge. North America was divided into two parts. During this period, a vast quantity of marine reptiles inhabited the enormous sea, something that is proved by numerous fossils. When the expanses of water finally began to recede, numerous lakes and swamplands evolved, providing the last of the dinosaurs with an ideal habitat. The decline in sea levels brought about major changes on land.

Plant in the Cretaceous (pine)

The Cretaceous (144–65 million years ago)

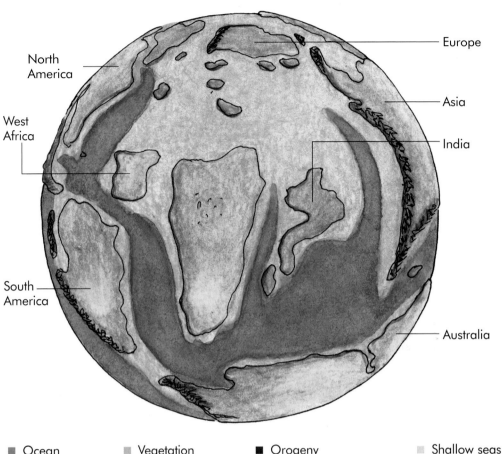

North America
Europe
West Africa
Asia
India
South America
Australia

■ Ocean ■ Vegetation ■ Orogeny ■ Shallow seas

In the following period, America's two major mountain ranges formed, the Rocky Mountains and the Andean Cordilleras. In Europe, which was divided into northern and southern halves, similar processes occurred. This was the start of the formation of today's Alps.

These tectonic changes and changes in sea levels also brought changes to the climate. While the global climate was well-balanced during the Jurassic period, temperatures generally dropped in the Cretaceous. Different climatic zones developed. The flora of these regions also underwent a change. With the gradual decline in sea levels, the land became increasingly dry. The once rampant forests turned into savannahs where horsetail and ferns flourished. In higher regions, conifers and ginkgo trees could be found.

Later, the first shrubs and fast-growing flowering plants began to grow in the clearings that were once woodland and the home of huge plant-eating dinosaurs. Small broad-leaved trees and mixed conifer woods gradually evolved. These became even more prolific in the Tertiary.

Based on the fossilized plants that have been found in certain layers of sediment, scientists can now determine which climate prevailed in the various epochs of the geological eras in the respective regions.

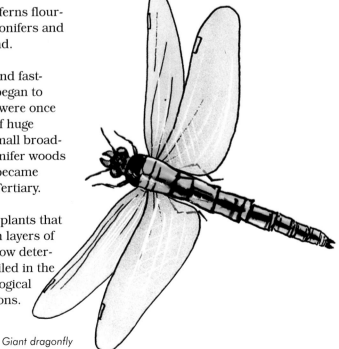

Giant dragonfly

Styracosaurus

Order: Ornithischia
Suborder: Ceratopsia
Family: Ceratopsidae

Styracosaurus

The horned dinosaurs (Ceratopsia), to which the Styracosaurus belongs, were among the last species of dinosaur to develop in the late Cretaceous. They lived for only 20 million years before dying out. During this period, they spread across large parts of Asia and North America.

The well-armoured Styracosaurus (Greek styrax = lance), which was indigenous mainly to North America, grew to a length of approximately 5.2 metres. It moved on all fours and reached a maximum speed of between 20 and 25 kilometres an hour.

The most striking feature of the Styracosaurus was its long, straight, upward-pointing nose horn. It had two smaller protrusions located

directly between its eyes. A collar-shaped frill consisting of hollow bones covered with muscles and membrane surrounded the head with long, ray-like spikes.

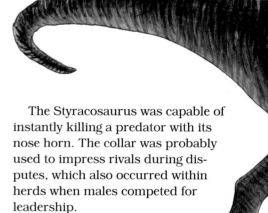

The Styracosaurus was capable of instantly killing a predator with its nose horn. The collar was probably used to impress rivals during disputes, which also occurred within herds when males competed for leadership.

If serious disputes had occurred, the spikes on the collar would not have survived any great impact. It is more likely that the collar acted as a visual warning and was probably used

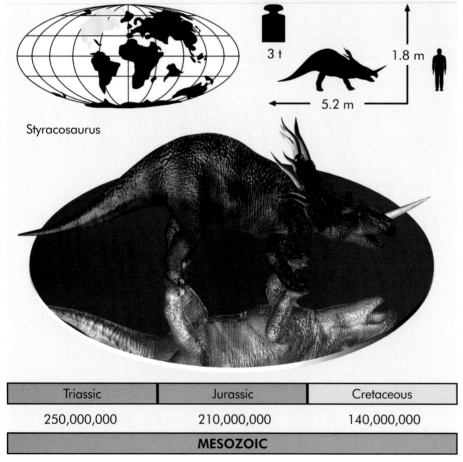

Styracosaurus

3 t   1.8 m

5.2 m

Triassic	Jurassic	Cretaceous
250,000,000	210,000,000	140,000,000
MESOZOIC		

during the rutting season when the males courted the favour of the females.

With its horny beak, which consisted of two sharp-edged curved halves, the Styracosaurus could tear off and crush even the toughest plant parts. It found these in higher wooded areas, where the Styracosaurus lived in huge herds.

Pachycephalosaurus

The Pachycephalosaurus was a "dome-headed" dinosaur. They belonged to the Ornithischia family (bird-hipped dinosaurs), with the suborder Ceratopsia as a sister group. The Pachycephalosaurus was considered the giant of its family. Like all bird-hipped dinosaurs, this animal also fed exclusively on plants.

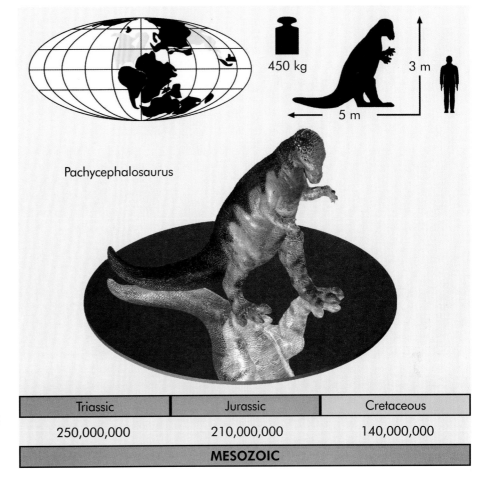

450 kg

3 m

5 m

Pachycephalosaurus

Triassic	Jurassic	Cretaceous
250,000,000	210,000,000	140,000,000
MESOZOIC		

Pachycephalosaurus

Order: Ornithischia
Suborder: Pachycephalosauria
Family: Pachycephalosauridae

It walked on two legs and reached speeds of between 25 and 35 kilometres an hour. The length of its body measured almost five metres, its skull around 60 centimetres. The dome-shaped skullcap, which was approximately 25 centimetres thick, gave the Pachycephalosaurus an unusual appearance. It had bony knobs around the back of its skull, rather like a ruff, and some on its snout.

After the first finds were made, it was initially believed that this strange-shaped skull was the result of some terrible disease. The skull, however, probably played an important role in combat.

This occurred when rival males fought over territory and female animals clashed. Standing at a distance and in an upright position so as to look as threatening as possible, they charged towards each other with bent heads and erect tails. They probably rammed each other with their robust skulls but without causing any serious injury. The territory and herd were ultimately left to the animal with the greatest stamina. The skulls of females were not so strong.

The Pachycephalosaurus was found primarily in North America and Asia, which at that time belonged to Laurasia. It lived there in the highlands, where it grazed like herds of goats and sheep today.

Skull of Triceratops

Triceratops

The Triceratops belonged to the order of bird-hipped dinosaurs (Ornithischia). It was one of the last of the Ceratopsia (horned dinosaurs) and lived 76 to 65 million years ago in the late Cretaceous. Its name stems from the Greek: tri- = three, kéras = horn; óps = face, hence three-horned face. It was given this name in 1889 by the American scientist O. C. Marsh.

The heaviest member of its family, Triceratops was up to nine metres long and three metres tall, weighing in at up to 8.5 tons. Strong, sturdy legs supported its enormous body. The tail was short and heavy, its skin leathery. Its two-metre-long skull bore a short, thick nose horn. On each side of the nose horn were two upward-pointing brow horns. The large bony frill around its neck was covered with skin and rimmed with bony bumps, making the Triceratops look very menacing. If it lowered its head to attack, Triceratops was a force to be reckoned with.

Triceratops was a herding animal and roamed the western parts of North America. Here, it fed on herbaceous plants, which it bit off with its parrot-like, tooth-lined jaw. If its beak wore down, a new one grew in its place. Triceratops needed large quantities of food to sustain itself, so

Triceratops – finds in North America

was forced to wander extensively during periods of drought.

Sixteen different types of Triceratops have since been described. They differ mainly in terms of the structure of the skull. Some of these differences probably represent various stages of development or are gender-specific. Therefore the actual number of species is probably smaller.

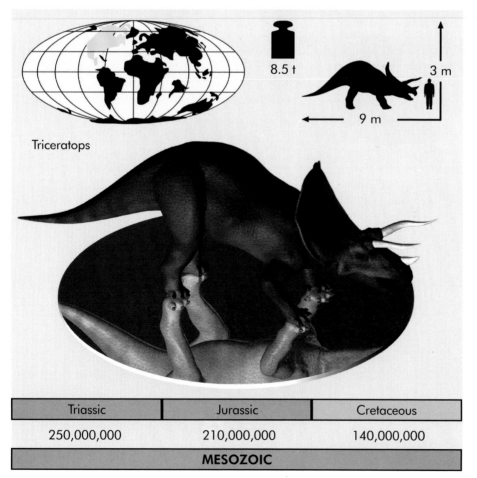

Triceratops

Triassic	Jurassic	Cretaceous
250,000,000	210,000,000	140,000,000
MESOZOIC		

Triceratops

Order: Ornithischia
Suborder: Ceratopsia
Family: Ceratopsidae

Hypsilophodon

The Hypsilophodon (high-crested tooth) lived 120 million years ago in the early Cretaceous. It belonged to the suborder Ornithopoda (bird-footed dinosaur) of the order of Orni-thischia (bird-hipped dinosaurs). It was a common animal resembling today's tree kangaroo, although this species lived on the ground.

The swift two-legged herbivore was 2.3 metres long and weighed 50 kilos and was therefore relatively small and agile. It was of slight build, its skeleton consisting of thin-walled, hollow bones like those of the gazelle. The short thigh bone was supported by strong muscles, enabling it to change directions rapidly. Long, thin feet ended in thin toes with short, sharp claws. The feet gave the Hypsilophodon balance but also enabled it to move quickly.

The otherwise defenceless animal probably protected itself by running away. Its long tail gave it balance. The Hypsilophodon was probably able to dart sideways or change direction quickly like a hare. It may have had two rows of bony plates running down its back. It lived with others in a group.

Twenty well-preserved skeletons were found on the Isle of Wight. The herd is thought to have been caught in quicksand where it perished.

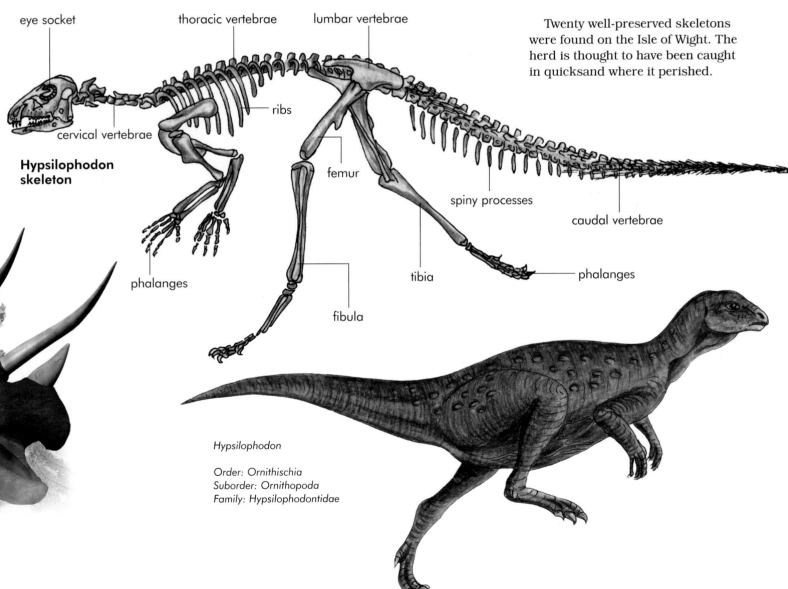

eye socket

thoracic vertebrae

lumbar vertebrae

ribs

cervical vertebrae

Hypsilophodon skeleton

femur

spiny processes

caudal vertebrae

phalanges

tibia

phalanges

fibula

Hypsilophodon

Order: Ornithischia
Suborder: Ornithopoda
Family: Hypsilophodontidae

Deinonychus

The discovery of the extensive remains of a Deinonychus in Montana, North America in 1964 was the cause of some surprise. Until then, experts had believed that this animal, which belonged to the order of Saurischia (lizard-hipped dinosaurs), was a slow-moving scavenger whose sluggishness prevented it from catching prey itself.

Researchers discovered that this was a lightly built animal, about 3.4 metres in length, which could run as fast as an ostrich (up to 40 kilometres an hour). It grew to a height of about 1.8 metres and weighed 70 kilograms. Its teeth were serrated and bent inwards so that large chunks of meat could be torn out of the captured animal.

Its slender legs had long shanks, the hind feet four toes, including one vestigial toe. The weight of the body was carried by the third and fourth toe. The second toe was equipped with a large, sickle-shaped claw, over ten centimetres long. This claw gave the Deinonychus its name, which means "terrible claw" (deinos = terrible; onychus = claw).

The Deinonychus used the claw to lash out at its prey but it could be retracted during running so that it no longer touched the ground. The claw on the other foot and the long tail, which was reinforced by bony rods, gave the animal balance. The front limbs were equipped with three fingers, each with long, curved claws which were held close to the body, similar to the wings of birds.

Deinonychus

Order: Saurischia
Suborder: Theropoda
Family: Dromaeosauridae

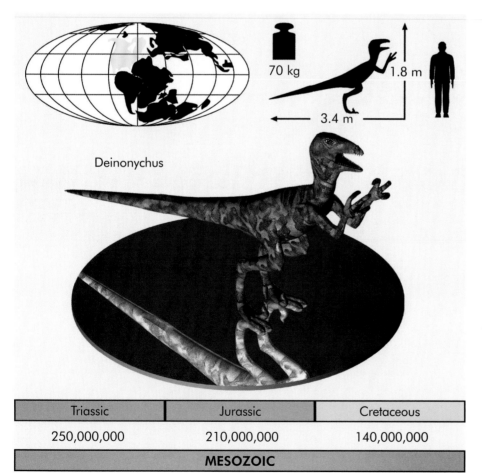

70 kg   1.8 m   3.4 m

Deinonychus

Triassic	Jurassic	Cretaceous
250,000,000	210,000,000	140,000,000
MESOZOIC		

Found next to five Deinonychus skeletons were the bones of an over seven-metre-long herbivore known as Tenontosaurus. It is unclear whether the Deinonychus herd encircled and overwhelmed this far larger animal by pouncing on it and injuring it with their strong claws, or whether the Tenontosaurus killed some of the smaller meat-eaters and then died of its injuries. When alone, the Deinonychus normally fed on lizards.

In search of food in the mountains of North America, whole herds of Deinonychus could pounce as fast as ostriches on other dinosaurs and injure or kill them with their sharp claws.

Tyrannosaurus

Tyrannosaurus rex belonged to the order of lizard-hipped dinosaurs. It lived 67 to 65 million years ago in the late Cretaceous. Its name comes from the Greek "tyrannos" meaning "tyrant".

Probably the most famous of all dinosaurs, the Tyrannosaurus rex could reach a length of over 12 metres and a height of six metres, weighing over seven tons. Its torso was short and its pelvis long and slender to provide support for the muscles in its long, powerful legs.

To be able to move its huge body, Tyrannosaurus needed large, strong muscles to bend and stretch its limbs. The soft mass of muscles was naturally destroyed during fossilization. However, it is still possible to see where the muscles joined the bones and determine the arrangement of muscles in relation to those of today's animals.

Tyrannosaurus moved on two column-like hind legs, each equipped with three toes. The fourth toe did not quite touch the ground. Crooked tarsal bones provided additional support. Experts believe Tyrannosaurus could run up to 25 kilometres an hour. The front limbs were short. They were equipped with two toes which were so stunted they did not even reach the mouth. They might have helped the animal stand up, something that was only possible if the Tyrannosaurus bent its head into the back of its neck.

The first reconstructions showed the tail trailing along on the ground behind the Tyrannosaurus. The upper part of the body stood upright. Nowadays, experts believe the upper part of the body was held in an almost vertical position and the tail was held aloft to provide balance.

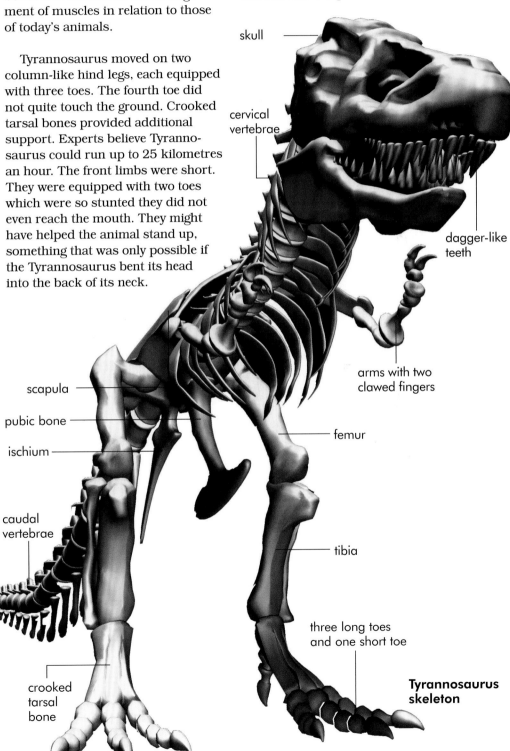

skull

cervical vertebrae

dagger-like teeth

arms with two clawed fingers

scapula

pubic bone

ischium

femur

caudal vertebrae

tibia

crooked tarsal bone

three long toes and one short toe

Tyrannosaurus skeleton

71

Tyrannosaurus

Order: Saurischia
Suborder: Theropoda
Family: Tyrannosauridae

This was made possible by long processes on the caudal vertebrae. These provided support for strong muscles which could lift the tail. Tyrannosaurus was probably able to move the tip of its tail in all directions.

No other dinosaur had such a large, strong head as Tyrannosaurus. A bony crest on the animal's skull

Opinions differ greatly about the Tyrannosaurus' diet. Was it really a killer machine or did it merely scavenge for food? Today, the general consensus is that the Tyrannosaurus fed on large herbivores. Even large specimens such as Triceratops were not safe from Tyrannosaurus. It probably had well developed senses

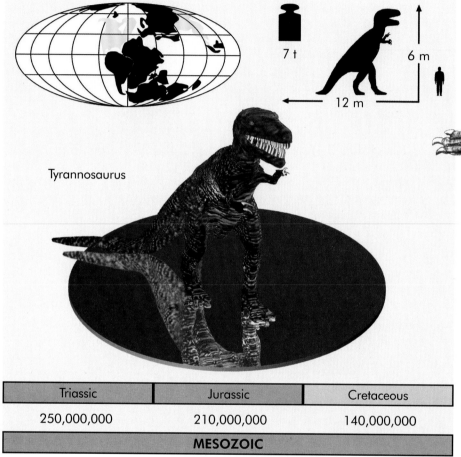

Tyrannosaurus

7 t

6 m

12 m

Triassic	Jurassic	Cretaceous
250,000,000	210,000,000	140,000,000
MESOZOIC		

saurus used its claws to pin it to the ground. Now it could tear out pieces of meat with its sharp, slightly backward-leaning teeth. It also devoured smaller dinosaurs in one piece. To catch its prey more easily, the Tyrannosaurus may have pursued herds of dinosaurs and killed the sick, weak animals. When the Tyrannosaurus opened its enormous mouth and let out one of its ear-splitting roars, this almost certainly scared off rivals.

In one week, the Tyrannosaurus needed approximately as much food as its own body weighed, which is why few other dinosaurs were able to survive in the same environment. There was simply not enough food to go around. The estimated life expectancy of a Tyrannosaurus was around 30 years. It died out at the end of the Cretaceous together with all other dinosaurs.

provided support for strong jaw muscles. The one-and-a-half-metre-long skull contained a large, slightly protruding mouth with numerous teeth which were up to 20 centimetres long. They were dagger-like and increased in size towards the back of the mouth. Once they were worn out, new ones grew in their place.

which helped it hunt. Experts believe its eyes were not positioned on the side of its head but faced forwards so that Tyrannosaurus had depth perception and a wide visual field which enabled it to spot its prey. Once an animal was caught, the Tyranno-

Edmontosaurus

Order: Ornithischia
Suborder: Ornithopoda
Family: Hadrosauridae

Edmontosaurus

Edmontosaurus lived approximately 76 to 65 million years ago in the late Cretaceous. It belonged to the sub-order Ornithopoda ('bird feet') of the order of Ornithischia (bird-hipped dinosaurs). Edmontosaurus was the largest of the duck-billed dinosaurs (hadrosaurs), but was probably slow and defenceless.

The plant-eating Edmontosaurus moved predominantly on four legs, grew to a length of up to 13 metres and weighed up to 4 tonnes. In spite of its size, it could reach speeds of between 14 and 20 kilometres an hour. The Edmontosaurus lived on land and only ventured into water when pursued by predators. Other-wise, it roamed fertile country in herds.

As the fossilized stomach contents of some duckbilled dinosaurs have shown, the Edmontosaurus fed mainly on the tough, woody parts of plants such as bark, pinecones and branches. It could tear these up with its wide, flat, horn-covered beak and push them to the back of its mouth with its strong tongue. It had hundreds of cheek teeth, which

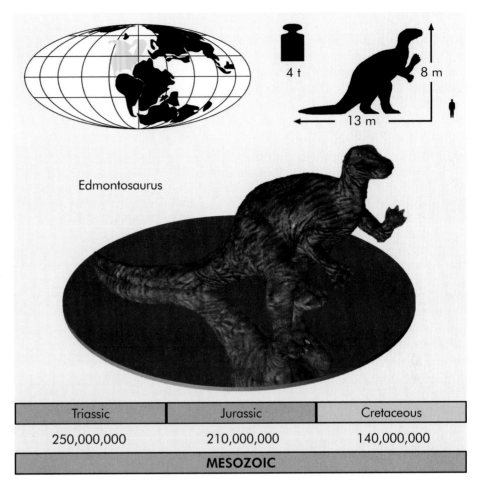

Edmontosaurus

4 t   8 m   13 m

Triassic	Jurassic	Cretaceous
250,000,000	210,000,000	140,000,000
MESOZOIC		

crushed food effectively. Once they were worn out, new ones grew in their place. The Edmontosaurus also had cheek pouches, which prevented food from dropping out of its mouth when chewing. Other reptiles do not have such an advantage. When a tortoise eats grass, for example, half of it drops out of the sides of its mouth. The outside surface of the teeth of the Edmontosaurus did not wear down as fast as the inside surface, which meant it used the external surface to bite off plants and the inner surface to grind them.

In some Edmontosaurus fossils, mud has penetrated the skull and fossilized there, providing an impression of the brain. This has shown that the sections responsible for sight, hearing and smell were well developed. Based on the size of the eye sockets, it is assumed that the eyes of the Edmontosaurus were ten centimetres in diameter. A large opening for the optic nerve suggests that the dinosaur had good vision.

The bones in front of the eyes contained small openings where salt glands might have been located, as is the case in reptiles and birds today. Through the tear fluid, these glands secrete superfluous salt taken into the body in the animal's often salty diet.

The snout on the long head sported a fleshy flap of skin which might have stood up like a cockscomb or which Edmonto-saurus was able to inflate like a balloon. It may have used this flap to communicate with animals of the same species, possibly through colour or noise. It might also have attracted females by issuing a piercing cry. The Edmontosaurus lived and nested in large groups, caring for its young until they were old enough to look after themselves.

Corythosaurus

Corythosaurus belonged to the duck-billed dinosaurs which were members of the Ornithischia order (family of Hadrosauridae). Like all duck-billed dinosaurs, the Corythosaurus ran on two long hind legs when in danger. Its tail helped it keep its balance. Otherwise it moved on all fours. Its feet were equipped with hoof-like nails.

Its body was nine metres long and it weighed 3.5 tons. A particularly striking feature of the Corythosaurus was the shape of its skull. Between its eyes from the ridge of its nasal bone was a bony, hollow crest which contained respiratory tracts linking the top of the crest with the snout.

Because the animals usually stayed near or in water, a theory developed that these crests were air chambers which helped the Corythosaurus breathe when it was swimming and eating. This proved to be incorrect because the animals probably inhabited pine and magnolia forests where they found most of their food alongside plankton. It is now thought that the hollow areas in the bone were important for noise production. With bellows that probably resembled the sound of a fog-horn, the animals could communicate with each other over long distances. It is possible that different herds communicated with each other and not just animals within the same herd. These noises were used as a warning device but also to scare off or intimidate rivals such as the big meat-eaters.

Corythosaurus

Order: Ornithischia
Suborder: Ornithopoda
Family: Hadrosauridae

Corythosaurus is thought to have had a keen sense of smell, which enabled it to pick up the scent of enemies in time. Their vision was also very well developed. Their eyes had a diameter of ten centimetres offering them a particularly wide angle of vision.

In North America, where the Corythosaurus was mainly found, researchers discovered that crest sizes could differ significantly. This suggests there were either different

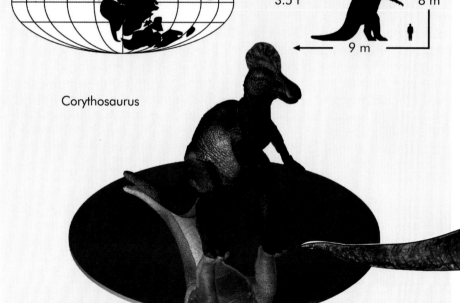

Corythosaurus

3.5 t

8 m

9 m

varieties or these animals were in different stages of development. Females also had smaller crests.

Triassic	Jurassic	Cretaceous
250,000,000	210,000,000	140,000,000
MESOZOIC		

Iguanodon

Iguanodon was named after the iguana from tropical America (plus Greek: odous = tooth). It lived from the late Jurassic period (Malm) until the Lower Cretaceous, 130 to 115 million years ago. The Iguanodon belonged to the order of Ornithischia (bird-hipped dinosaurs) and is the most famous of the Ornithopoda ('bird feet').

Part of an Iguanodon bone was found in southern England in 1809. In 1811, more bones and teeth were discovered. The teeth were initially believed to be those of a huge mammal. Mantell, a keen fossil collector and geologist, eventually identified them as those of a reptile. Because they reminded him of a kind of iguana, he gave the animal the name Iguanodon in a scientific treatise in 1825. At the time, he described the animal as a dragon-like creature with a lizard-like head and a horn on its nose. This horn, however, later turned out to be the thumb of the Iguanodon.

Iguanodon

Triassic	Jurassic	Cretaceous
250,000,000	210,000,000	140,000,000
MESOZOIC		

Today, we know that the Iguanodon was a plant-eater with a compact body and a long, powerful tail. Its hind legs were long and strong, each foot equipped with three hard, hoof-like nails. The shorter front legs, which were designed for snatching, had five flexible fingers, three of which had nails. The thumbs each had a dagger-like spike, which enabled the Iguanodon to grasp objects. It is possible that the spike was also used as a weapon against rivals, the big carnivores such as the Megalosaurus.

The Iguanodon usually roamed the tropical landscape of the Cretaceous on all four legs. It generally travelled in a group, searching for horsetails and ferns on the banks of lakes and rivers. The Iguanodon could also rear up on its hind legs to reach higher plants. Its tail supported it and helped it balance. The Iguanodon's head had an extended snout with a beak-like jaw. With its many cheek teeth, it had no difficulty biting off and crushing tough-fibred plants.

Twenty-nine almost completely preserved skeletons were found in 1922 in a coal mine near Bernissart in Belgium. Footprints were discovered in southern England.

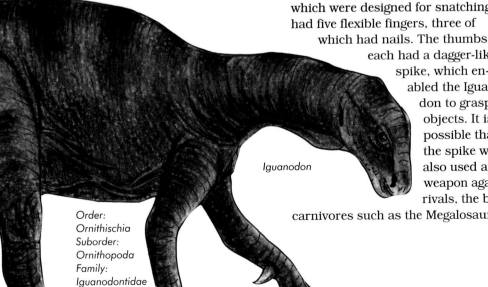

Iguanodon

Order:
Ornithischia
Suborder:
Ornithopoda
Family:
Iguanodontidae

75

Parasaurolophus

The Parasaurolophus was one of the most remarkable duck-billed dinosaurs (Hadrosauridae) and one of the best-adapted of the Ornithopoda, the plant eaters of the order of Ornithischia (bird-hipped dinosaurs).

clear today. It may have been used to enhance the dinosaur's voice, like the pouches of skin in other duck-billed dinosaurs. The trumpet-like noise that was produced may have been important in courtship rituals. It may also have been used as a warning device or to frighten predators. It is also conceivable that the cavity allowed air to

more profusely in the late Cretaceous and the delicate shoots of conifers. It had no teeth at the front of its beak but several rows of molars in the back of its upper and lower jaw, which grew again when worn down.

The Parasaurolophus grew to a length of ten metres and weighed roughly two and a half tons. It usually moved on all four legs but was also able to stand up in dangerous situations and escape on two. The long wide tail helped it keep its balance in this position.

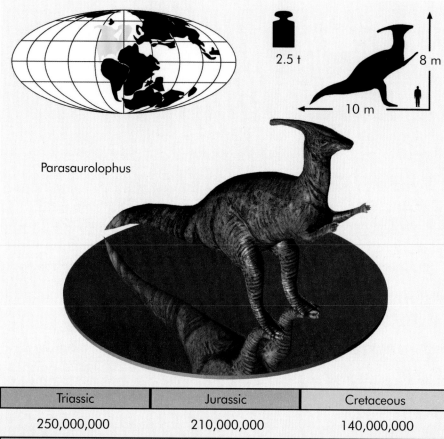

2.5 t

8 m

10 m

Parasaurolophus

Parasaurolophus

Order: Ornithischia
Suborder: Ornithopoda
Family: Hadrosauridae

Triassic	Jurassic	Cretaceous
250,000,000	210,000,000	140,000,000
MESOZOIC		

The most striking feature of the Parasaurolophus was its backward-pointing bony crest. A nose crest, which consisted of a hollow double tube, ran from its nostrils to the end of the crest and from there back to the skull. It was over 1.5 metres long. The fossilized crest of other Parasaurolophus specimens were much shorter, perhaps because it was female. Its function is still not

circulate in the skull in order to cool the brain.

The animal's snout and hollow crest were more slender than those of the hadrosaurs whose crests were hard and bony. With its duck-like beak, the Parasaurolophus was able to pick off the fibrous flowering plants that grew

The first Parasaurolophus finds were made in 1923 in Alberta, Canada, but fossilized remains were also unearthed in Utah and New Mexico. It lived in the late Cretaceous period 76 to 74 million years ago.

Velociraptor

The Velociraptor was one of the fiercest predators in the late Cretaceous period 84 to 80 million years ago. It belonged to the family of Dromaeosauridae from the order of Saurischia (lizard-hipped dinosaurs).

During a joint Polish-Mongolian expedition, the first and only evidence of fights between dinosaurs was found in 1971. A Velociraptor lay on the ground, its claws still behind the neck frill of its enemy. The two rivals lay near a nest containing the eggs of a Protoceratops. The Velociraptor was probably taken by surprise. During the struggle, a huge hurricane must have occurred and both dinosaurs were killed. They were preserved by layers of desert sand. At 1.8 metres long, the Velociraptor was an agile sprinter with its long legs and light bones.

It lived in herds with members of its own family. With its long legs, strong teeth and sharp claws, it had no problems catching and dissecting its prey.

Like the North American Deinonychus, the Velociraptor of Mongolia had three claws on each hand. Small, sickle-shaped claws also existed on the hind legs. In other respects too, there was an astonishing similarity between the animals although they lived 20 to 30 million years apart.

Velociraptor

Order: Saurischia
Suborder: Theropoda
Family: Dromaeo-
sauridae

15 kg   1.6 m
1.8 m

Velociraptor

Triassic	Jurassic	Cretaceous
250,000,000	210,000,000	140,000,000
MESOZOIC		

It is conceivable that that representatives of these groups found a way from North America to Asia. Although the Pacific Ocean separated the two continents, migration might have been possible via land bridges (Beringia).

Ankylosaurus

The largest of the armoured bird-hipped dinosaurs (Ornithischia) of the Ankylosauridae family was the Ankylosaurus. Its name "stiff lizard" comes from the bony plates, humps and spikes that covered its body. It lived in the late Cretaceous in North America. It probably originated in Asia where several different but similar specimens were found. It is possible that they migrated here from the Far East via land bridges.

The Ankylosaurus was a bulky reptile weighing up to 6 tons and reaching a length of up to eight metres. Its skull was wide, its back

Ankylosaurus

Order: Ornithischia
Suborder: Ankylosauria
Family: Ankylosauridae

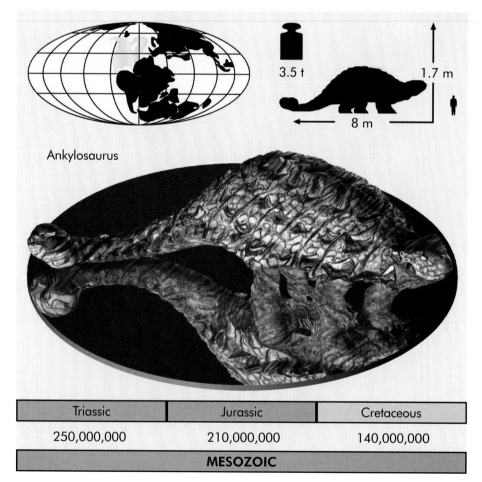

3.5 t

1.7 m

8 m

Ankylosaurus

flat. Its extremities were very short, which meant the Ankylosaurus was unable to run very fast. It was protected by its indestructible armour, which ran the length of its body from head to tail. This consisted of several hundred individual plates embedded in the skin, which made the armour flexible.

In the event of danger, the Ankylosaurus simply pressed itself against the ground. Its only defensive weapon was a kind of bony club at the end of its tail, with which it could lash out on all sides and seriously injure enemies.

Numerous, incomplete Ankylosaurus skeletons have been found, which is why reconstructions are often very different. More recent depictions show that the armour was less regular and also studded with numerous spikes. Little is known about the Ankylosaurus' diet.

Triassic	Jurassic	Cretaceous
250,000,000	210,000,000	140,000,000
MESOZOIC		

The Ankylosaurus was one of the last of the dinosaurs, becoming extinct towards the end of the Cretaceous period.

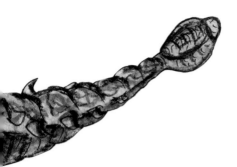

Dromaeosaurus

The Dromaeosaurus, which is one of the lizard-hipped dinosaurs (Saurischia) was discovered for the first time in 1914 in Canada. It was initially unclear as to whether it belonged to the Coelurosauria (dinosaurs with long necks, small skulls and a slight build)

15 kg

1.3 m

2 m

Dromaeosaurus

Triassic	Jurassic	Cretaceous
250,000,000	210,000,000	140,000,000
MESOZOIC		

Dromaeosaurus was most common during the Upper Cretaceous, living in herds in North America.

or the Carnosauria (short-necked, large, heavily built dinosaurs).

It was not until the Deinonychus was discovered that experts realized the Dromaeosaurus possessed features from both groups: the slight build of the Coelurosauria and the heavy skull of the Carnosauria. In the meantime, we know that this animal was roughly two metres long and very agile. It had well-formed sickle-shaped claws on its toes. The second claw was particularly useful for its predatory lifestyle. Its hands were also equipped with sharp claws. With its sharp, dangerous teeth, it had no difficult tearing apart its prey.

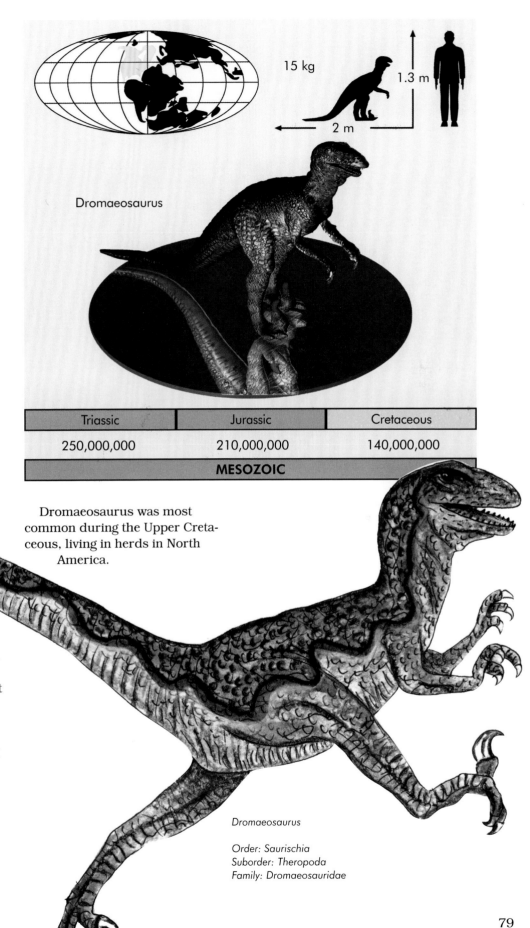

Dromaeosaurus

Order: Saurischia
Suborder: Theropoda
Family: Dromaeosauridae

Pteranodon

For many decades, the Pteranodon was believed to be the biggest flying reptile. It had a wingspan of seven metres and lived around 70 million years ago in the late Cretaceous. Pteranodon's body length measured

its hollow bones only five millimetres thick. Its skeleton was therefore very fragile. The animal weighed just 15 to 17 kilograms. It is surprising the animal did not break into pieces when it landed.

Pteranodon was probably a glider, allowing itself to be carried by up-currents. This has been determined on the basis of calculations of its weight and wing area. To reinforce wing movements, the shoulder girdle was joined to the spinal column and was not just connected by muscle, like other flying animals. The flying reptile needed two seconds for every flap of the wing.

Its habitat was primarily coastal regions where it hunted for fish which it caught with its long beak. The catch was stowed in a large pouch in its throat without upsetting the Pteranodon's balance during flight.

"Pteranodon" means "winged and toothless"; having no teeth, it gulped down its prey whole. On the ground, the Pteranodon was less flexible and able to move only very awkwardly.

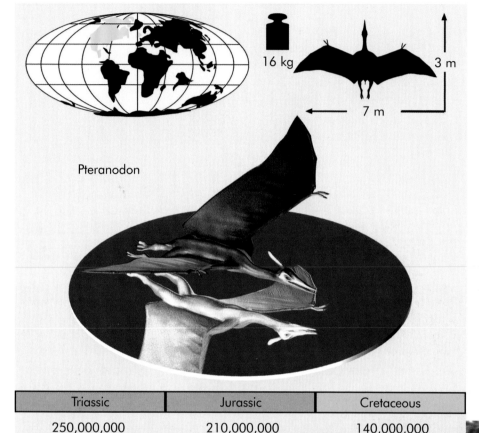

16 kg

3 m

7 m

Pteranodon

Triassic	Jurassic	Cretaceous
250,000,000	210,000,000	140,000,000

MESOZOIC

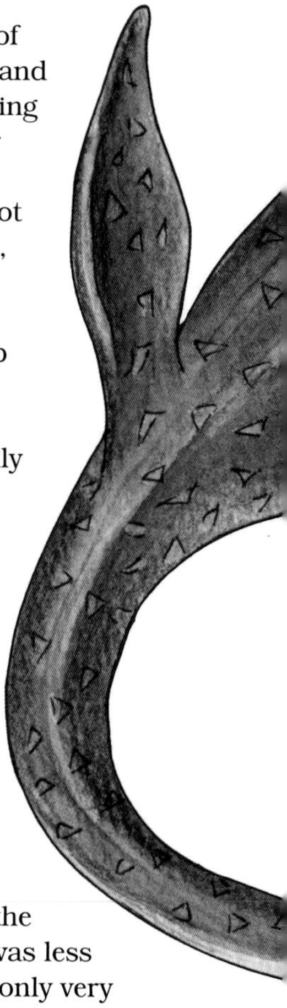

Pteranodon
Flying reptile

Order: Pterosauria
Suborder: Pterodacty-
loidae

a total of three metres, 1.8 metres of which consisted of a large head and a long, sharp beak. A thin bony crest protruded from its head, 60 centimetres long and 30 grams in weight.

This may have helped the Pteranodon steer when it was flying but almost certainly acted as a counterweight when it turned its head to the side. It may also have served to distinguish between males and females. The body of Pteranodon was no bigger than that of a turkey,

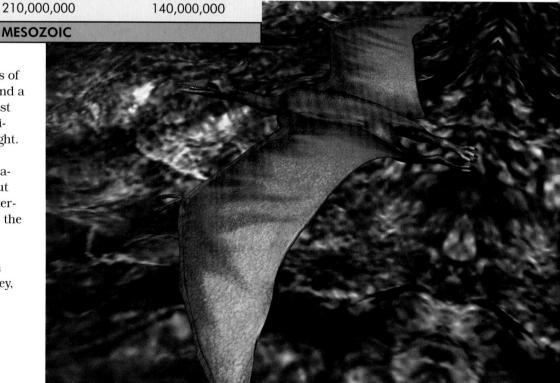

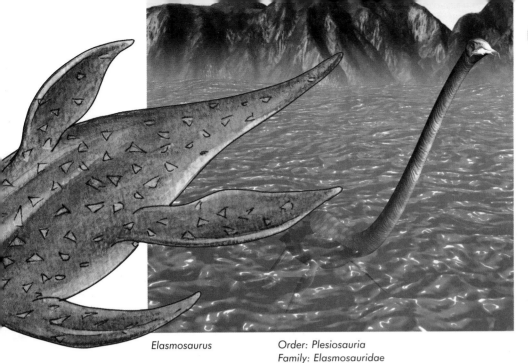

Elasmosaurus

Order: Plesiosauria
Family: Elasmosauridae

Elasmosaurus

Among the swimming reptiles of the Mesozoic was the very common group of Plesiosauria. The Elasmosaurus (Greek:

élasma = plate) belonged to this order. It was found above all in sediments from the late Cretaceous in Kansas in North America.

Altogether 12 metres long, its neck with 72 cervical vertebrae made up almost half of its total length. Its torso had only 24 vertebrae, its tail 21. Elasmosaurus had a very small head (60 centimetres long) and a jawbone lined with very sharp teeth. It probably fed on small fish which it caught near the surface of the water with swift movements of the neck. Similar marine reptiles found in Germany contained the remains of fish and flying reptiles which support this theory.

Instead of limbs, Elasmosaurus had four long flippers like all Plesiosaurs, which it moved up and down, just as birds move their wings. At the end of these flippers, finger and toe

bones were discernible, consisting of up to 10 bones.

Because the flippers could only be lifted to shoulder height, it was

very difficult for the animal to dive in deep waters. Shoulder and hipbones were flat like a plate so that the strong muscles attached to the bones provided a link to the flippers, making paddling efficient.

To lay its eggs, the Elasmosaurus had to go ashore – no easy task. After hatching, the young had great difficulty returning to the water and were frequently killed on their way there by other predators.

The Elasmosaurus died out at the end of the Cretaceous. Since they survived for several million years, the disappearance of the Plesiosauria remains a mystery, especially since other reptiles such as lizards, snakes and crocodiles have survived until the present day.

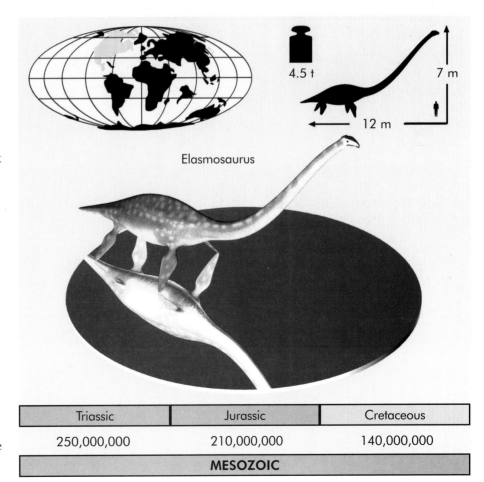

4.5 t

7 m

12 m

Elasmosaurus

Triassic	Jurassic	Cretaceous
250,000,000	210,000,000	140,000,000
MESOZOIC		

Ichthyosaur

One of the most famous fish-like marine reptiles is the Ichthyosaurus. It had an astonishing similarity to today's dolphins. It is unclear how this group evolved. They possibly descended from land reptiles. In the Triassic, however, they were only able to move in water.

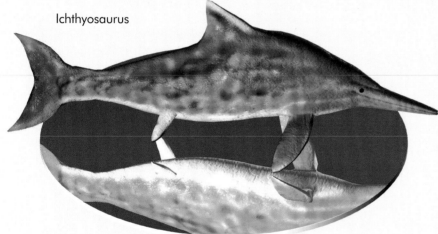

Ichthyosaurus

0.9 m

2 m

Triassic	Jurassic	Cretaceous
250,000,000	210,000,000	140,000,000
MESOZOIC		

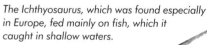

The Ichthyosaurus, which was found especially in Europe, fed mainly on fish, which it caught in shallow waters.

Numerous fossilized Ichthyosaurus skeletons were found in Holzmaden, a small town in Baden-Württemberg, Germany, in Posidonien slate (bedrock) which formed in the poorly aerated water (shallow seas). Hundreds of skeletons were found here, some so well preserved that the individual bones were still joined together. Several of them contained up to four small skeletons, proving that these "fish-lizards", as they are referred to, gave birth to live young. One fossil find even shows the Ichthyosaurus giving birth. This is how we know that the young left the birth canal tail-end first.

An examination of the contents of the stomach, which were also found, provided information about diet. The

nostril

Ichthyosaurus skeleton

eye socket

Ichthyosaurus
Marine reptile

Order: *Ichthyosauria*
Family: *Ichthyosauridae*

preferred food of the Ichthyosaurus was fish, but it also ate marine animals such as octopus.

The Ichthyosaurus was two metres long (other marine reptiles

a triangular-shaped fin on its back. Its five fins helped it steer. The tail fin, the lower part of which contained the bent spinal column, was used for propulsion. Pigment tests carried out on the remains of skin that were found revealed that the Ichthyosaurus was brownish or dark green in colour.

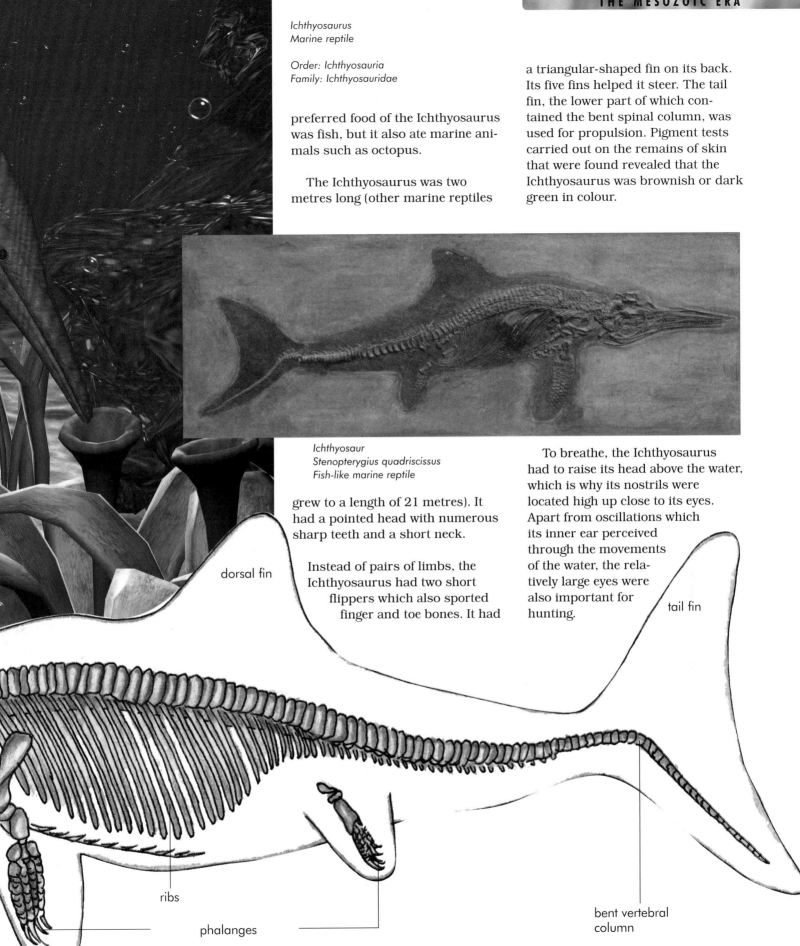

Ichthyosaur
Stenopterygius quadriscissus
Fish-like marine reptile

grew to a length of 21 metres). It had a pointed head with numerous sharp teeth and a short neck.

Instead of pairs of limbs, the Ichthyosaurus had two short flippers which also sported finger and toe bones. It had

To breathe, the Ichthyosaurus had to raise its head above the water, which is why its nostrils were located high up close to its eyes. Apart from oscillations which its inner ear perceived through the movements of the water, the relatively large eyes were also important for hunting.

dorsal fin

tail fin

ribs

phalanges

bent vertebral column

83

Gallimimus

The Gallimimus ("rooster mimic") was one of the largest of the Ornitho-mimidae ("bird mimics"). It belonged to the lizard-hipped dinosaurs (Saurischia) and lived 75 million years ago in the late Cretaceous.

This two-legged animal was four metres long and weighed 225 kilograms. At the end of its long legs were extended feet, which were well adapted to running. A long, rigid tail helped the animal maintain its balance when running. The front limbs each had three fingers, which the Gallimimus used to put twigs as well as small animals into its mouth.

Gallimimus had a toothless beak similar to that of ducks and geese. It only ate what it could swallow whole.

The Gallimimus inhabited inland riverbanks where periods of rain and drought alternated. Duck-billed dinosaurs and armoured dinosaurs also frequented such spots.

One of its arch-enemies was the fast-moving Deinonychus, which caught the Gallimimus with its strong claws. If it faced such an enemy, Gallimimus could only seek safety in flight.

Three completely preserved skeletons were found in the Gobi desert.

In 1965, part of another bird-like but much larger dinosaur was found. Even a forearm bone was 2.5 metres long up to the tip of the fingers. A single finger bone was 25 centimetres long and probably bore a huge claw. The genus has the name Deinocheirus ("terrible hand").

Gallimimus lived with other members of its family on the plains of Mongolia. There, it fed on insects and small animals. It may have been an expert opener of dinosaur eggs.

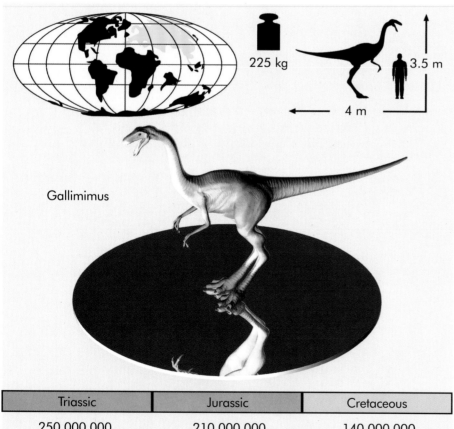

225 kg

3.5 m

4 m

Gallimimus

Later findings showed that they reached a length of 11 metres, a height of 4 metres and a weight of over 6 tons.

Triassic	Jurassic	Cretaceous
250,000,000	210,000,000	140,000,000
MESOZOIC		

Spinosaurus

The Spinosaurus was a huge, two-legged predator of the suborder Therapoda and order of lizard-hipped dinosaurs (Saurischia). It lived in the late Cretaceous period 100 to 95 million years ago.

The Spinosaurus was scientifically mentioned for the first time in 1915 after parts of its skeleton were found during an expedition to Egypt. However, these bones went missing during the Second World War. Other fossils were found in North Africa and in Niger (West Africa).

Between 12 and 18 metres long, the Spinosaurus was one of the biggest carnivores of its time. A particularly impressive feature was the sail-like fin on its back, which was almost two metres high. It consisted of bony rods which came from extended processes in its spinal column. These were covered with membrane. The sail was very similar to that of the Dimetrodon. It is not completely clear what the purpose of this strange construction was. It may have been colourful and helped attract females.

Another explanation might be that it helped the dinosaur regulate its body temperature. If the Spinosaurus exposed it to the sun, it could warm up quickly and stimulate circulation. Conversely, it could hold its sail in the wind to cool down. Other authors believe the spines formed a hump, similar to the one of a bison. Obviously, the spines increased the weight of the Spinosaurus considerably: its total weight was an estimated seven to nine tons.

The body of the Spinosaurus was voluminous, the jaw similar to that of a crocodile. Unlike other large meat-eaters, however, its teeth were straight, not curved. The Spinosaurus may have fed primarily on fish. The slightly larger hind legs suggest that the animal sometimes ran on two, sometimes on four legs.

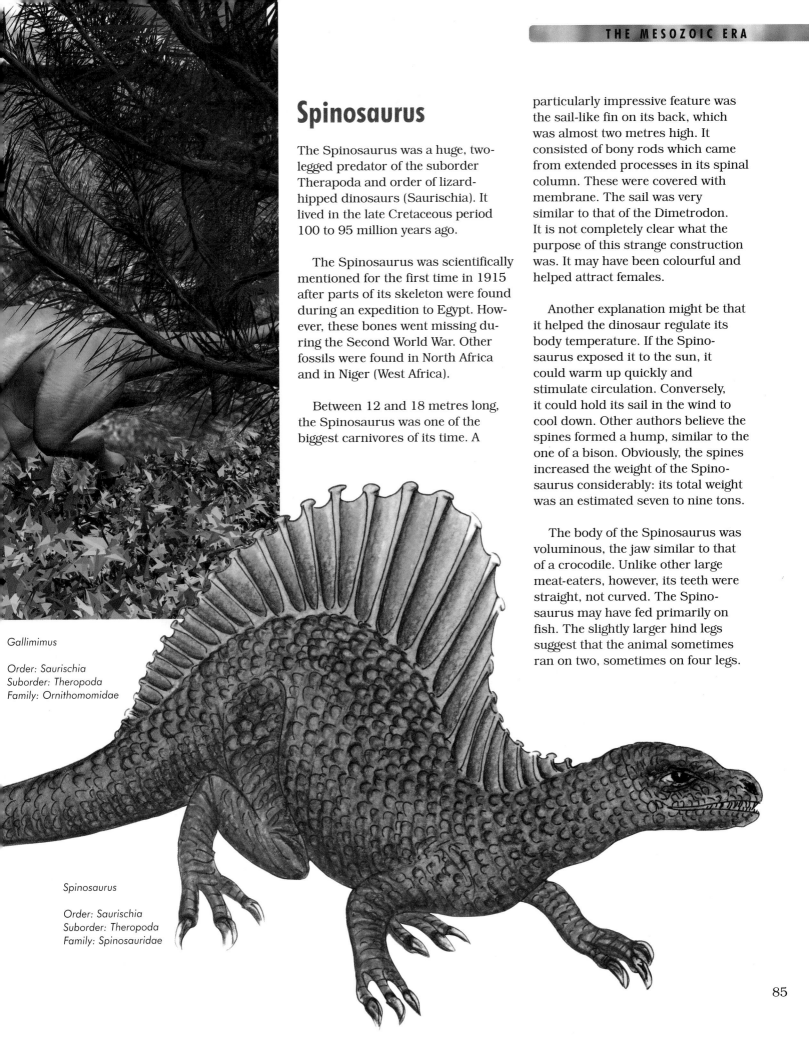

Gallimimus

Order: Saurischia
Suborder: Theropoda
Family: Ornithomomidae

Spinosaurus

Order: Saurischia
Suborder: Theropoda
Family: Spinosauridae

CHAPTER **5**

The Cenozoic Era

The most recent era in the Earth's geological history, the Cenozoic, began about 65 million years ago. It is subdivided into the Paleogene, Neogene and the Quaternary. After the extinction of numerous animal groups at the end of the Cretaceous, other species were able to flourish: the Age of the Dinosaurs was followed by the Age of the Mammals. They ranged from the whale to the rhinoceros, from the mammoth to the mouse. Slowly they colonized every habitat, the forests and steppes, the water and the air. They had of course to adapt their body structures and limbs to these diverse habitats.

In respect of reproduction, mammals fall into two groups: some lay eggs, and suckle their young after they have hatched, while others give birth to live young. Finally, the early primates gave rise to the primeval forms of the modern human species. The earliest known fossil finds suggest that the earliest hominids lived more than six million years ago, but primates' ancestry goes back to the Upper Cretaceous period over 80 million years ago.

Major geological events took place in recent times, including new orogenies (mountain formations), the rise of salt deposits nearer to the surface, and the Ice Ages of the Pleistocene epoch two million years ago. Repeated folding of the Earth's crust, frequent volcanic activity, and constant advances and retreats by the seas gradually produced the Earth as we know it today. It became colder in the polar regions, and the generally warm climate became increasingly seasonal.

The Paleogene and the Neogene

The Paleogene period, which began about 65 million years ago, is divided into three epochs.

The first part of the Palaeogene is divided into the Palaeocene, Eocene and Oligocene. The second part, or Neogene, comprises the Miocene and Pliocene. While the end of the Neogene period was previously dated to 600,000 years ago, the modern consensus is that the boundary with the Quaternary should be put at 2.5 to 2 million years ago.

The Palaeogene is characterized in particular by important deposits of mammalian fossils on land, but also in the sea. Orogenies and distur-

Scallop

bances of the Earth's crust resulted in the Alps, the Pyrenees, and the Himalayas etc. Volcanic activity was frequent during this period. Deposits in shallow seas resulted in today's Paris Basin and Upper Rhine Valley.

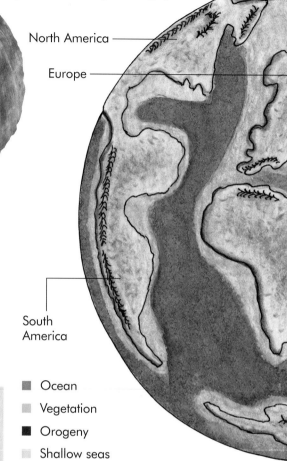

Paleogene and Neogene (65–2 million years ago)

North America

Europe

South America

- ◼ Ocean
- ◻ Vegetation
- ◼ Orogeny
- ◻ Shallow seas

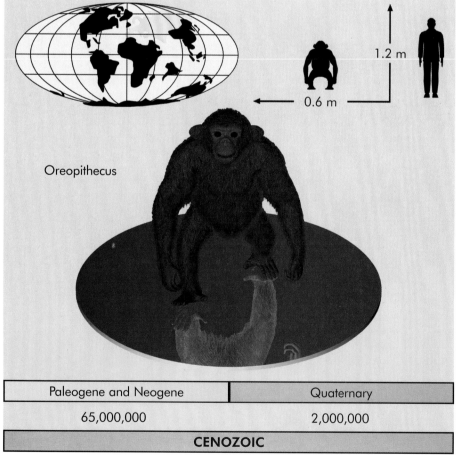

Oreopithecus

1.2 m

0.6 m

Paleogene and Neogene	Quaternary
65,000,000	2,000,000
CENOZOIC	

The fossils are very different from those of the Cretaceous, and reflect the explosion in mammal numbers. Mammals spread over the whole Earth, adapting themselves to the different situations on land, in the water and in the air.

The Palaeogene mammals included primitive, rodent-like forms, marsupials and insect-eaters. The ancestors of the carnivores and the forerunners of the ungulates (Condylarthera) were very like each other. They had somewhat clumsy bodies, dog-like heads with a small brain, robust limbs with five toes and thick claws. Major differences between

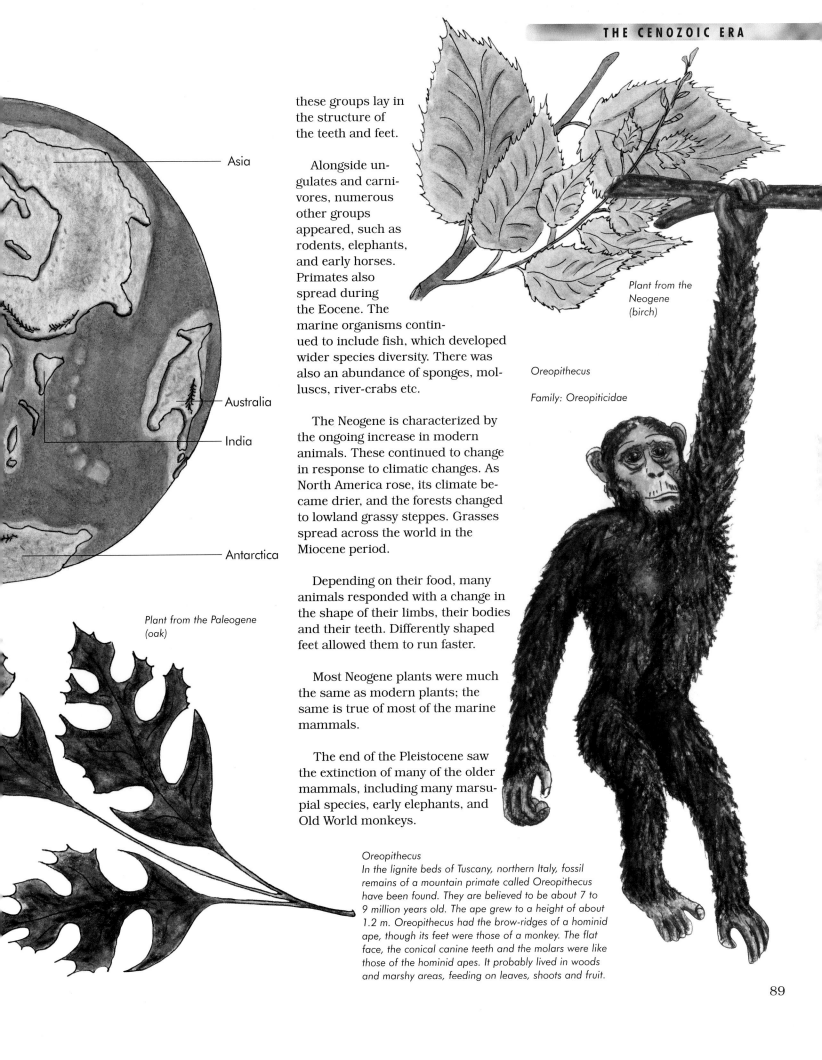

Asia

Australia

India

Antarctica

these groups lay in the structure of the teeth and feet.

Alongside ungulates and carnivores, numerous other groups appeared, such as rodents, elephants, and early horses. Primates also spread during the Eocene. The marine organisms continued to include fish, which developed wider species diversity. There was also an abundance of sponges, molluscs, river-crabs etc.

The Neogene is characterized by the ongoing increase in modern animals. These continued to change in response to climatic changes. As North America rose, its climate became drier, and the forests changed to lowland grassy steppes. Grasses spread across the world in the Miocene period.

Depending on their food, many animals responded with a change in the shape of their limbs, their bodies and their teeth. Differently shaped feet allowed them to run faster.

Most Neogene plants were much the same as modern plants; the same is true of most of the marine mammals.

The end of the Pleistocene saw the extinction of many of the older mammals, including many marsupial species, early elephants, and Old World monkeys.

Plant from the Neogene (birch)

Oreopithecus

Family: Oreopiticidae

Plant from the Paleogene (oak)

Oreopithecus
In the lignite beds of Tuscany, northern Italy, fossil remains of a mountain primate called Oreopithecus have been found. They are believed to be about 7 to 9 million years old. The ape grew to a height of about 1.2 m. Oreopithecus had the brow-ridges of a hominid ape, though its feet were those of a monkey. The flat face, the conical canine teeth and the molars were like those of the hominid apes. It probably lived in woods and marshy areas, feeding on leaves, shoots and fruit.

89

The Quaternary

The Quaternary is the most recent and also the shortest of the geological periods to date. It is divided into two epochs, the Pleistocene, which began between 2 and 2.5 million years ago, and ended roughly 10,000 years ago, when the present epoch, the Holocene, began.

The first glaciations happened in the northern hemisphere 600,000 years ago. This is why the start of the Pleistocene was once dated to this time. However, this glaciation had been preceded by a long cooling-

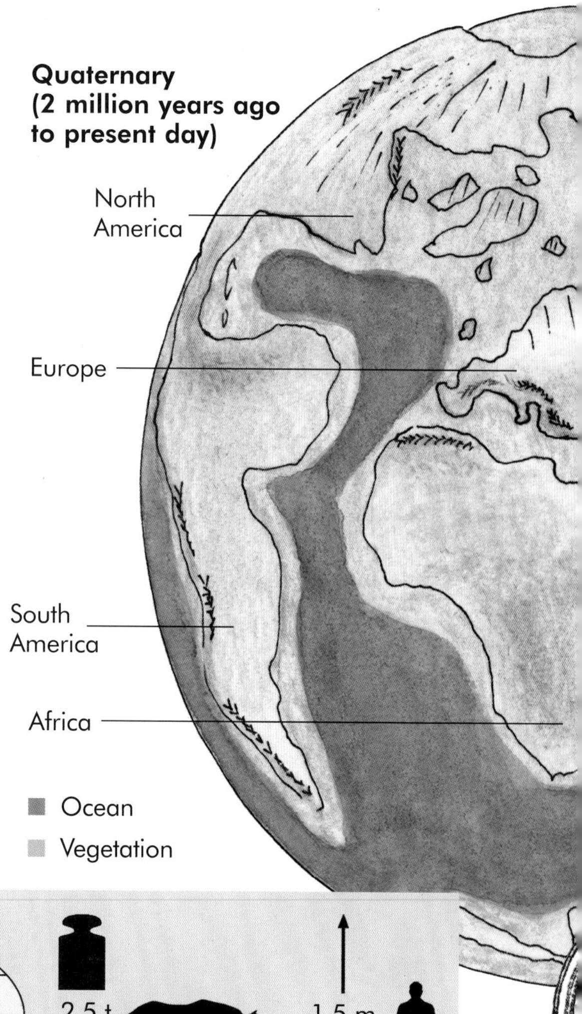

Quaternary (2 million years ago to present day)

North America

Europe

South America

Africa

■ Ocean
■ Vegetation

Woolly rhinoceros
(Coelodonta antiquitatis)

Suborder: Ceratomorpha
Family: Rhinocerotidae

Coelodonta was a woolly rhinoceros that grew to 3.5 metres in length. It had two horns on its nose, of which the front one in the male could grow to lengths of more than a metre. With its ragged fur, Coelodonta had adapted well to the raw climate of the steppe and tundra near the glaciers. Here it lived chiefly on leaves and grass.

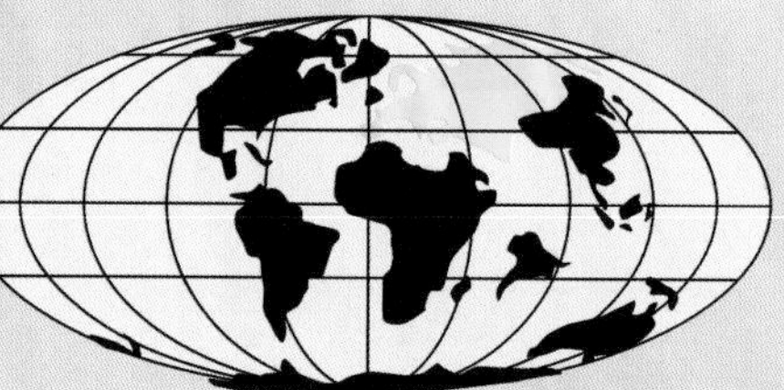

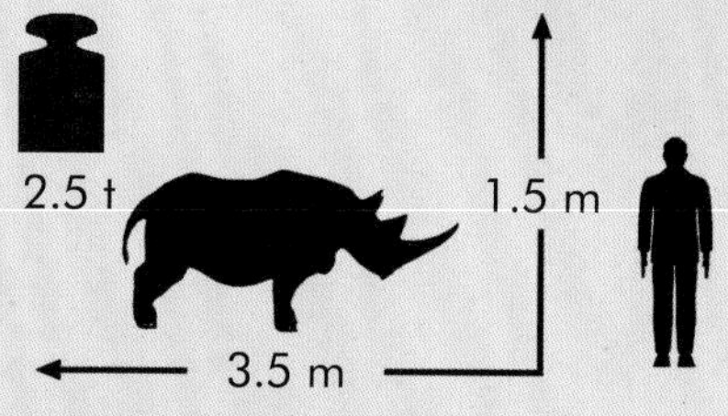

2.5 t   1.5 m
← 3.5 m →

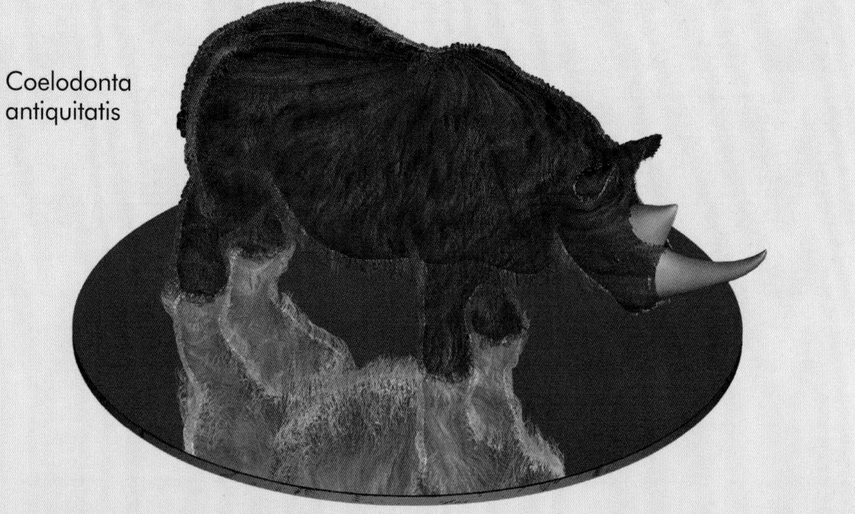

Coelodonta
antiquitatis

Although this period is very short in relation to the age of the Earth, it has a special importance for us, for it was the period during which the human species evolved.

Another reason for according it special attention is the changeability of the climate. For almost the whole of the Earth's history, the climate had been, at least in lower latitudes, evenly tropical and warm. It is only in the Quaternary that we see an alternation of warm and cold episodes.

Paleogene and Neogene	Quaternary
65,000,000	2,000,000
CENOZOIC	

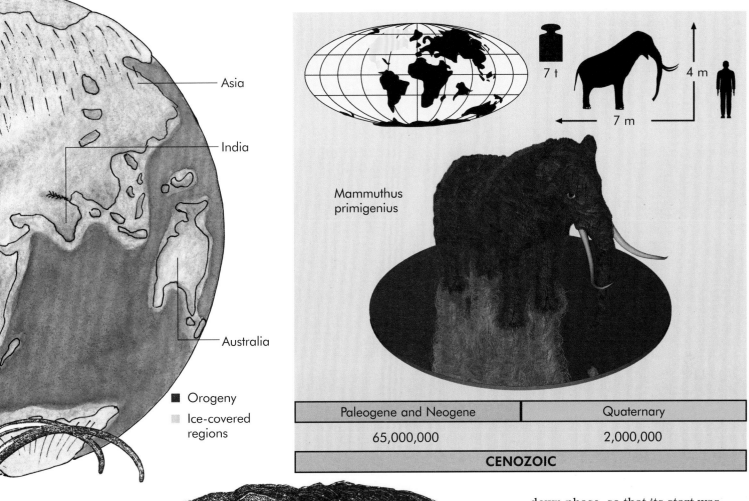

Asia

India

Australia

■ Orogeny
▨ Ice-covered
regions

Mammuthus
primigenius

7 t

4 m

7 m

Paleogene and Neogene	Quaternary
65,000,000	2,000,000
CENOZOIC	

down phase, so that its start was brought forward to two million years ago. During the cold episodes, major changes occurred in the flora and fauna, while the warm episodes were characterized by temperatures such as we have today.

Eurasia's flora was unable to spread southwards because its path was blocked by the insuperable glaciers of the Alps and the Carpathians. Only the hardiest species could survive the glaciations. In North America, species could branch out as far as the Gulf of Mexico, and when the glaciers receded, spread back northwards. As a result, the continent still has greater species diversity than Europe.

As reflected in its fossils, the fauna also responded to warm and cold episodes. Typical of the warm

The American mammoth, also known as the mastodon, appeared in the late Tertiary and had thick, ragged fur. It had two strong tusks pointing upwards, and stood about three metres high. In North America there were numerous coniferous forests where the American mammoth wandered around in herds. Picture of a mammoth dating from c. 1835 (woodcut).

episodes are the forest elephant and rhinoceros. The ancestor of our domestic cattle, the aurochs, likewise appeared in a warm episode. The cold episodes were the heyday of the mammoth, which had evolved from one branch of the elephants, the reindeer, and the woolly rhinoceros. Some individuals froze so quickly after death that the contents of their stomachs was preserved. Other species, such as carnivores and deer, survived both the warm and the cold episodes. Doubtless they undertook long migrations in order to find enough food in bad times.

The evolution of Man is also closely bound up with the Ice Ages. The deterioration in the climate and the advance of the ice masses, especially in the north, restricted the available living space, but at the same time new habitats were created by the lowering of sea-levels. There

Anancus, a forest elephant at home in Europe and Asia, was about three metres tall. It lived on the leaves of trees, but also on roots which it grubbed out of the ground. Anancus already looked very similar to modern elephants.

Anancus
(Miocene to Pleistocene)

Suborder:
Elephantoidea

Anancus

3 m

◄—— 7 m ——►

5 t

Homo neanderthalensis

In 1856 fossil remains of a prehistoric man were found in the Neanderthal valley near Düsseldorf in Germany. He is thought to have lived there around 100,000 years ago, during a warm interglacial period of the last Ice Age. The reconstruction of "Neanderthal Man" suggested a height of about 1.7 metres. He was squat, but powerfully built. His head was large, as were his hands. He had strong teeth, a flat nose, and pronounced browridges. Neanderthal Man already used tools. He probably died out about 30,000 years ago.

Paleogene and Neogene	Quaternary
65,000,000	2,000,000
CENOZOIC	

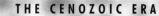

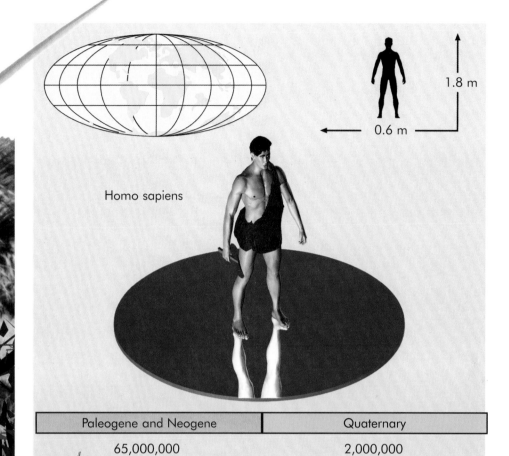

Homo sapiens

1.8 m

0.6 m

Paleogene and Neogene	Quaternary
65,000,000	2,000,000
CENOZOIC	

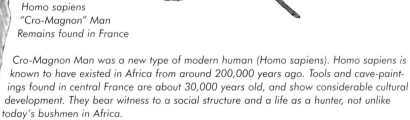

Plant in the Quaternary (birch)

was enough food in coastal areas in the form of fish, shellfish and marine mammals. Humanity was able to expand by settling the islands of south-east Asia and Australia, as well as America (via the Beringia land bridge).

The Holocene saw the ice masses begin to melt. New coasts formed, along with glacial moraines. Sea-levels rose, numerous low-lying areas turned marshy, while lakes dried out. Reforestation set in, with birch, pine, oak and beech.

As they evolved, people developed new lifestyles. Hunters and gatherers became sedentary farmers and stockbreeders, building homes and making clothes, in order to survive the last glacial periods.

*Homo sapiens
"Cro-Magnon" Man
Remains found in France*

Cro-Magnon Man was a new type of modern human (Homo sapiens). Homo sapiens is known to have existed in Africa from around 200,000 years ago. Tools and cave-paintings found in central France are about 30,000 years old, and show considerable cultural development. They bear witness to a social structure and a life as a hunter, not unlike today's bushmen in Africa.
About 10,000 years ago, people in many parts of the world developed new ways of life. They became farmers and stockbreeders, cultivating the fields. They thus became sedentary. This led to a population explosion which made Man the dominant species on Earth today.

GLOSSARY

Allosauridae
The largest carnivores of the late Jurassic. At 12 metres long, Allosaurus was the largest species and gave its name to the family.

Anchisauridae
The oldest prosauropods. They resembled the somewhat larger Plateosauridae.

Ankylosauridae
A family of Ankylosauria. They had a broad skull and a bony club at the tip of their tail, which they could use to seriously injure an attacker with sideswipes.

Brachiosauridae
A family of the suborder Sauropoda (e. g. Brachiosaurus).

Camarasauridae
A family of the suborder Sauropoda (e. g. Camarasaurus).

Ceratosauridae
A family of the infra-order Carnosauria, resembling the Megalosauridae but with a small horn or comb on their snout.

Condylarthera
Mammals of the Palaeogene with a somewhat clumsy body, a dog-like head and small brain, massive limbs with five toes, and very thick claws.

Diplodocidae
A family of the suborder Sauropoda (including Diplodocus, Apatosaurus, Mamenchisaurus).

Dromaeosauridae
Particularly rapacious predators. While they had the lightweight body structure of the Coelurosauria, they had the heavy skull of the Carnosauria.

Heterodontosauridae
A family of the suborder Ornithopoda (e. g. Pisanosaurus and Heterodontosaurus).

Hypsilophontidae
A family of the suborder Ornithopoda (e. g. Hypsilophodon).

Ichthyiosauria (fish saurians)
An order of the Saurian group. They lived in the Mesozoic era and resembled today's dolphins.

Iguanodontidae
A family of the suborder Ornithopoda. They had very squat bodies, went on all fours, and could only move slowly, but were able to stand on their hind-legs (e. g. Iguanodon).

Megalosauridae
A family of the infra-order Carnosauria. They had powerful bodies and a heavy head with numerous sharp teeth (e. g. Dilophosaurus and Megalosaurus).

Nodosauridae
A family of the order Ankylosauria. They had a narrow skull and a body armoured with bone, short legs and broad feet.

Ornithomimidae
A side-branch of the infra-order Coelurosauria. Similar to the modern ostrich, approx. 3.5 metres long, toothless, very fast runner with long legs (e. g. Gallimimus).

Pachycephalosauridae
A family of the Pachycephalosauria. In addition to a domed skull, they had collar-like excrescences on the sides and back of the head, (e. g. Pachycephalosaurus).

Plateosauridae
A family of prosauropods (e. g. Plateosaurus).

Podokesauridae
A family of the infra-order Coelurosauria. They were very active, nimble predators, moving their slender bodies on two legs. The long tail helped them keep their balance.

Prosauropodeae
A family of the suborder Sauropodomorpha. A branch of the suborder Sauropoda.

Ramphorhynchoidea
An early, primitive group of pterosaurs.

Sauropoda
An order of saurian families including the largest animals ever to walk on land. With a small head, a long neck, a large body with thick legs and a long tail. Important families were the Brachiosauridae, the Diplodocidae, the Camarasauridae and the Titanosauridae.

Spinosauridae
A family that probably developed from the Megalosauridae, with a dorsal sail or comb (e. g. Spinosaurus).

Titanosauridae
The last family of the suborder Sauropoda. They lived for about 80 million years until the end of the Cretaceous (e. g. Titanosuchus).

Tyrannosauridae
Very large Theropoda on dry land (e. g. Tyrannosaurus).

INDEX

PHOTO IMAGES:

Fotolia.com: p. 6 (© Anna Kasatkina)

All other images:
Archives of contmedia GmbH